Healthy Eating

THE AUSTRALIAN
Women's Weekly

Healthy Eating

acp
books

contents

detox

We all want to enjoy good health, unlimited energy, restful sleep and a sense of serenity. But increasingly the world around us presents us with some real challenges in realising these goals.

We may find ourselves relying on convenience food to meet our nutritional needs because we're working longer hours. Is it any wonder, then, that our freezers tend to be stocked with frozen dinners or other convenience-oriented food, or that we find ourselves dialling take-away more often than is healthy? And, even if we try to improve our diet, buying natural produce and ingredients isn't as easy as it once was. Many supermarket shelves are stocked with foods grown or raised with the use of pesticides and antibiotics, that contain artificial additives or preservatives, or have had much of the goodness processed out of them.

At the same time, the water that comes out of our taps contains chemical contaminants, and the air we breathe is polluted with toxins from industry, transportation and even the cleaning products we use around our homes.

These all have toxic effects – the Environmental Protection Agency in the United States considers that 60 per cent of all herbicides, 90 per cent of all fungicides and 30 per cent of all insecticides are potentially carcinogenic (cancer-causing). It's been estimated that, on average, we eat or drink about 3.75 litres of pesticides, take in five kilograms of chemical food additives and breathe in two grams of solid pollution every year.

cleanse, energise, pamper

WHY YOU NEED TO DETOX

Besides external sources, toxins in our body can result from viral or bacterial infections, or from the by-products of the metabolism of certain bacteria and yeasts that inhabit our bowel. As if this isn't enough for our bodies to deal with, nearly all of us find ourselves locked into a hyperactive state, with very little time to spend in a healing state, where we can let go of stress. We also relegate stress-beating exercise to the bottom of our to-do list.

To fight this combination of challenges, many of us turn to medical or recreational drugs to combat ills or help us unwind. But, ironically, these further pollute our bodies, causing more toxins and stress. Unfortunately, the payoff for our 21st-century lifestyle is excess weight, allergies, headaches, fatigue, rashes, colds, coughs and a host of other ailments.

Yet there is some good news. Our body is an incredible feat of biomechanical engineering. All we need do is give it the tools – and that includes a 'detox' – to repair the damage wreaked by an overload of toxins, and it will put us back onto the path to wellbeing.

What we need is a program that will cleanse and energise our body and mind, and help us build a healthy lifestyle – and that includes some self-pampering.

The benefits are many: increased energy, glowing skin, healthier hair and nails, less anxiety, better concentration, better metabolism and bowel patterns and, in the long-term, a slowing down of the ageing process and a lower risk of both minor illnesses and chronic disease.

HOW YOU KNOW YOU NEED TO DETOX

If you are in tune with your body, you will often feel when it's not running smoothly. But even if you've lost touch with your personal rhythms, your body will send you plenty of signals that it needs a detox tune-up. (See the 'symptoms' checklist, opposite.)

> Detoxing can be challenging, so choose a time that works for you.

WHEN TO DETOX – AND WHEN NOT TO

Detoxing can be challenging, so choose a time that works for you. The start of spring, summer or autumn are best, because you don't need as much food to refuel your body as you do in winter, and detox foods tend to be light. Ideally, you should also choose a time when you're not under a lot of pressure or, better still, when you have a few days off – it's important that you take it easy.

Directly after a bout of the flu or food poisoning is a bad time to detox. So, wait until you've had sufficient time to recover. You may also want to delay starting a detox program if you are feeling emotionally vulnerable – such as if you've just ended a relationship or moved house.

While many people choose the longer detox programs – seven days or two weeks – you should be aware that you may face some hurdles in maintaining your busy schedule. For example, you may develop a detox headache and find it difficult to concentrate. We recommend that you don't take painkillers because they add to your toxic load.

Be aware that withdrawal headaches from caffeine, which is on the 'foods to avoid' list (page 11), can be particularly vicious on the second day. You'll need to make sure you drink plenty of water and that, if you want to, you can lie down until the effects of the headache subsides.

If you feel light-headed on a detox program never drive a car or operate machinery. Rest is the best remedy. Also, avoid very hot baths and showers, as these not only reduce your energy, but may increase your blood pressure.

We recommend you stop the detox program immediately if you feel sick, light-headed or dizzy, or if you have a constant headache or muscle pain that you would rate as severe. Don't feel discouraged. You can always embark on the program again when you feel more able.

PREPARING TO DETOX

You'll notice that we've included some 'day before' advice in the one-week detox menu, and some 'two-days before' guidelines for the two-week program. That's because you need to ease into the program to reduce sudden withdrawal symptoms.

If you drink six cups of coffee a day and go straight onto water or herbal tea, we're pretty sure you're going to have a headache that will put you off ever undertaking a detox program again. A week before you're due to start detoxing, cut your caffeine intake by a cup a day. If you drink alcohol or eat a lot of sugar, drink or eat them less and less as the days to your detox approach.

Setting up your environment to detox is also very important. Throw out any foods that are full of sugar, caffeine, white flour or saturated and trans fats (a 'bad' fat that raises cholesterol levels; usually found in cakes, biscuits and table margarines).

Ask yourself if that king-sized chocolate bar will survive your detox or whether you'll be tempted by that cup of coffee. Remember, after you've finished your detox, you'll be making healthier food choices. You'll need to replace unhealthy foods with healthy ones – lots of fruit and vegetables, filtered water, herbal teas and pulses and grains. See our menus (pages 20-23) and make a shopping list. Wherever possible, buy organic so your body won't have to deal with the chemicals used on commercial fruits and vegetables.

You'll also need some essential kitchen tools: a steamer and juice extractor (borrow one if you haven't got one), for example, so you can get the benefits of freshly squeezed oranges, lemons, pineapples and more.

HERO DETOX FOODS

Apples   Contain vitamin E, which improves endurance and stamina of muscles and nerves, and protects the respiratory system from toxins. Also a good source of vitamins A and C, biotin, folic acid and quercetin, an antioxidant that helps lower fat and cholesterol.

Beetroot   Reputed to be one of the best liver-cleansing vegetables, it also helps nourish the nervous system and brain with manganese, magnesium and folate.

Broccoli   Is high in folate and vitamins A and C, as well as calcium and phosphorous, which help build and maintain strong bones. It also stimulates the liver.

Cabbage   High in vitamin C and calcium. An excellent source of chlorine and sulphur, which expel waste and cleans the blood.

Carrots   Packed with nutrients including vitamins A and C; believed to cleanse, nourish and stimulate the body, particularly the liver, kidneys and digestive system.

Celery   A recognised diuretic and laxative, and the richest vegetable source of sodium with more than 120mg per 100 grams.

Cherries   Food for the blood with iron, copper and manganese, plus vitamins A and C. They help remove toxins from the kidneys, liver and digestive system. Cherries also contain a phytochemical called ellagic acid, which could help protect against cancer.

Chickpeas   A good source of fibre and calcium for healthy bones, phosphorous for healthy kidneys and nerves, and potassium, which nourishes muscles.

Cucumber   Contains high levels of vitamin E, essential for healthy heart muscles, and iodine for healthy hair, nails, skin, teeth and thyroid function. Also helps prevent water retention.

Fennel   A diuretic that can also help settle the stomach.

Garlic   A powerhouse of sulphur, a natural penicillin that helps keep the body alkaline. Garlic oil contains a substance that helps clear the respiratory and lymphatic system.

Ginger   Cleans, stimulates and rejuvenates the digestive system.

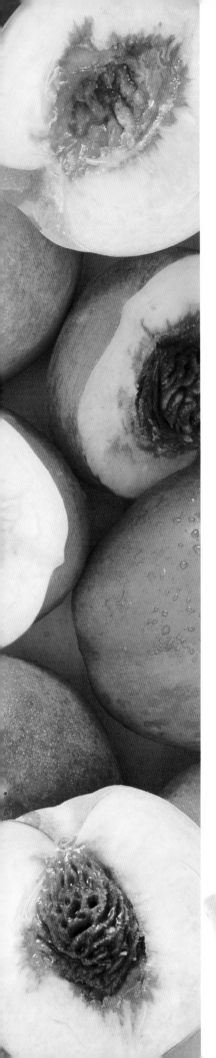

Grapes Contain ellagic acid that may have anti-carcinogenic effects. Also contains high levels of manganese, the 'memory mineral', which nourishes the nervous system, helps maintain sex hormone production and assists in the formation of healthy red blood cells. A good source of silicon, which helps circulation, prevents nervous exhaustion and is essential for healthy skin, hair and teeth.

Lemons Are an excellent source of phosphorous, required for the repair and healthy functioning of the nervous system. Also a good source of sodium, which assists in the proper elimination of waste and cleansing of the lymphatic system, and helps stimulate the liver and gallbladder. Freshly squeezed lemon juice in warm water (ratio 25/75) first thing in the morning is a great way to pep up your liver.

Melons High in sodium to help cleanse the kidneys. Also contain a host of other minerals including calcium, phosphorus, potassium, iron and zinc, as well as vitamins A and C.

Onions A good source of silicon, which can promote better blood circulation and prevent nervous and mental fatigue. Also contain potent antiviral and antibacterial nutrients.

Oranges Loaded with vitamin C, with an average of 30-50mg/100g of freshly squeezed juice. Also contain calcium and phosphorous, which, when combined, help protect the body from infections and viruses.

Papaya One of the richest sources of the enzyme papain, which is essential to protein digestion. Also an excellent source of vitamins A and C.

Parsley Stimulates the kidneys to eliminate toxic waste.

Peaches A good source of vitamin A, important for healthy skin, good eyesight and protection from the effects of stress and environmental toxins. Vitamin A also protects the lungs and respiratory tract from infection. Contain sulphur, which can help expel harmful mucus from the body.

Pears Contain alkaline-healing and cleansing minerals including potassium, sodium, iron calcium, magnesium and manganese. Also contain sodium, which not only benefits the lymphatic system, but is required regularly for proper elimination of carbon dioxide waste from the lungs.

Pineapples Contain bromelain, which has anti-inflammatory properties and helps the body digest protein.

Sea vegetables Alginic acid, found in some seaweeds, binds with heavy metals, such as cadmium, lead, mercury and radium, to eliminate them from the body.

Strawberries Contain ellagic acid that may have anti-carcinogenic effects. Weight for weight, contain 1½ times as much vitamin C as most citrus fruits and are also a good source of iron.

Tomatoes Contain chlorine, an acid mineral that stimulates the liver to filter out waste products. Helps with the production of gastric juices, maintenance of correct fluid levels and the reduction of excess blood fat.

Watercress Reputed to cleanse the blood and improve the condition of the skin.

CLEANING UP

Ever wondered how the body disposes of the toxic waste accumulated in your system? Toxins are cleansed from the body in a variety of ways, but mainly through:

- your liver, for final elimination through your lungs, kidneys and intestines
- your lungs, which exhale poisonous carbon dioxide and other waste products
- your kidneys, which eliminate water-soluble toxins
- your intestines, which eliminate both water and fat-soluble toxins and wastes
- your skin, through perspiration
- your hair and nails, which eliminate some toxins, including heavy metals

OTHER EXCELLENT DETOX FOODS

Apricots An excellent source of vitamin A, and a good source of vitamin C and fibre.

Avocados Supply all the essential daily B-group vitamins as well as magnesium, calcium, phosphorous and potassium. Are a great source of 'good' fats, which help lower cholesterol and glutathione, an antioxidant that combines with fat-soluble toxins to make them water-soluble.

Bananas Very high in potassium, and a great source of the 'memory mineral', manganese, as well as iron and copper for healthy blood, magnesium, calcium and phosphorous, vitamins A and C, and some B-group vitamins.

Barley The wholegrain variety is a good source of B vitamins and also contains a host of minerals that are nourishing and cleansing. It is also high in fibre.

If it's fresh, organic and a fruit or vegetable, it's an excellent detox food.

Grapefruit A great source of vitamins C and E, and some of the B-group vitamins.

Lentils Very low in fat and full of iron, zinc, magnesium, vitamin A and B-group vitamins. Also high in fibre.

Lettuce Supplies more than 2000mg/100g of the mineral silicon, which helps promote calcium metabolism and eliminates excess uric acid deposits from the bone structure and bloodstream. Go for the darker green leaves.

Prunes Have high levels of magnesium, which have a natural laxative effect. Also a good supply of potassium. Help the blood become more alkaline.

Pumpkin An excellent source of bone-building silicon, as well as vitamin A, which is necessary for good vision, healthy skin and a strong immune system. Pumpkin is also a good source of vitamin C, potassium, iron and is high in fibre.

Spinach Contains chlorine, which regulates correct acid and alkali levels in the blood, as well as silicon, sodium, vitamins A and E, magnesium, manganese, copper and iron.

Sesame seeds An excellent source of protein, calcium, iron and magnesium. Also assist in the formation of blood platelets and, in combination with iron, have blood purifying qualities.

Tofu As well as being low in saturated fat and a vegetarian source of protein, tofu seems to have the ability to bind to heavy metals, so they can be eliminated from the body.

Yogurt Natural yogurt contains good bacteria that can help cleanse the digestive system and keep intestinal flora healthy.

FOODS TO AVOID

Toxins are harmful substances that affect the healthy functioning of our bodies. Most people are aware that their diet needs improving and, by controlling what they eat, they can control some of the toxins that enter their body.

The following should be regarded as 'toxins-on-a-plate': chemical preservatives, dyes, flavouring agents, additives, artificial sweeteners and hydrogenated vegetable oils. Make sure you avoid them.

Also avoid processed and refined foods that have had their natural nutrients stripped and destroyed. Wherever possible, a better choice is organic whole foods.

Most people who detox should also cut out meat, wheat and dairy. Naturopaths believe these foods create acid toxins that, in excess, can damage organs and glands, harm joints and arteries, and even inhibit immune responses.

Unfortunately, many dairy foods and meats now contain growth promoters, hormones and antibiotics that put a strain on the whole body. However, one exception is natural live yogurt, which has a soothing and nurturing effect on the digestive system, and can help keep healthy bacteria in the gut. We use sheep or goat's milk yogurt in our recipes, as these are much easier to digest and can aid digestive disorders and stimulate digestion.

Meat is also hard to digest, and is a major source of saturated fat, the kind that will contribute to blocked arteries and increase the risk of heart disease.

FOODS TO AVOID
- processed and refined foods
- hydrogenated vegetable oils
- wheat
- alcohol
- caffeine
- dairy
- fish
- salt
- sugar
- meat

You'll notice we don't include fish in our detox programs, because it can harbour unwanted pollutants. But, even though we want you to stick to a vegetarian diet while cleansing and re-energising your body, you may want to incorporate fish later into your diet, and so we have included fish in the 'before & after' section of the menus. In fact, most health experts recommend that you eat three servings of fish a week because of its ability to reduce the risk of heart disease, and auto-immune and joint problems.

Two other things you won't be allowed on a detox are wheat and alcohol. Wheat is a common allergen and wheat bran can inhibit the absorption of some important nutrients, as well as irritate the intestinal lining.

In large quantities, alcohol can be a toxic substance, and heavy drinking can harm the liver and deplete nutrients such as vitamins A and C and the B-group vitamins, as well as magnesium, zinc and essential fatty acids. It can lead to severe dehydration. Modern methods of producing alcohol also means it often contains chemical pesticides, colorants and other harmful additives.

Bad news for cappuccino addicts: caffeine is also on the 'foods to avoid' list, as are sugar and salt. Consuming an excessive amount of caffeine can result in insomnia, headaches and high blood pressure, as well as reducing the body's ability to absorb vitamins and minerals.

Of course, large amounts of refined sugar not only upset the balance of blood sugars in the body, but are full of empty kilojoules.

Salt is necessary to maintain normal hydration of the body's circulation and cellular fluids. However, many people eat too much salt, simply because food manufacturers tend to add salt to everyday foods such as bread, cereals and canned goods. Too much salt overloads the kidneys and can cause fluid retention, which may lead to heart failure, stroke, osteoporosis or kidney problems, including kidney stones.

In our detox recipes, we've used fresh herbs and lemon juice to add zest to food. We're sure you'll also find these healthier alternatives just as flavoursome.

> Rather than use salt, a better way to flavour foods and give it zest, is to add fresh herbs and lemon juice.

GETTING THE BALANCE RIGHT

The acid/alkaline level of the body (also known as the 'Ph' level) is important for healthy cells and tissues. For the body to function properly, it needs to keep its acid/alkaline balance within normal levels. If the body is too acid or too alkaline, cells can be damaged and tissues won't function effectively, thereby affecting your health.

Foods can affect the Ph level of the body (which is normally slightly alkaline), and diet appears to be one of the causes of an unbalanced Ph level. Some foods break down into acid-forming substances, while others break down into alkaline-forming substances. The diet of many people in Western countries consists of acid-forming food (saturated fats, sugar, meat, processed foods and refined products), therefore the body has a more acid Ph level than is healthy.

Your diet should be made up of 70 per cent alkali-forming foods and 30 per cent acid-forming foods. Alkaline-forming foods consist of most fresh fruits, including citrus, melons, pineapple, mango, kiwifruit and papaya, and vegetables, including asparagus, celery, spinach, carrot, onion, broccoli and potatoes (with the skin on). Acid-forming foods include meats, fish, poultry, eggs, cheese, bread, rice, oats, most cereals, lentils, sugar, walnuts and hazelnuts.

Naturopaths believe that keeping your body in an alkaline state will improve your mood, energy levels, sleep quality, and reduce aches and pains, headaches and, in the long-term, your risk of chronic disease.

Exercise also can affect the acid/alkaline balance of your body by making the blood more acidic. Deep breathing, on the other hand, makes the blood more alkaline.

H$_2$0

Drink like a fish during your detox, but make it nothing but juice, water and herbal tea. Sixty per cent of your body is made up of fluid, which is absolutely essential for the healthy functioning of your entire system. Fluids promote chemical reactions, lubricate joints, transport nutrients and are important for kidney and immune function, healthy skin, and even the prevention of pain.

You need to drink 1-1.5 litres of pure water a day. You can add a squeeze of lemon juice to it if you wish. And you'll find plenty of delicious juices included in the detox plans.

But don't just use water on the inside to purify your body. The section on External Detoxing (page 14) explains how to cleanse your body with H$_2$0 on the outside.

EXERCISE AND DETOX

True or false. If you swim, go for a run or have a workout at the gym, you will detox faster.

False. In fact, indulging in this sort of strenuous exercise while you're on a detox program could land you in hospital. A detox is not the time to run a marathon.

No matter what detox program you choose to undertake, it's important you get plenty of rest. If you're on the one-day detox program, the most strenuous thing you should do is have a massage. If you choose the weekend detox, a bit of gentle walking is the only exercise recommended. For the one- and two-week detox programs, two gentle walks a week are all you need to help eliminate toxins such as urea and lactic acid.

An alternative to walking is five or 10 minutes of gentle exercise, such as yoga, tai chi and chi gong. These exercises gently pump lymph, an alkaline fluid that removes acid waste from the blood and tissues, around the body. Gentle exercise also helps dissolve and eliminate crystalline acid deposits in the joints.

Remember, there is no compulsion to exercise. In fact, on the stricter fasts, experts recommend against it. If you feel you need extra sleep, or you simply want to lie down, it is important you follow your body's cues. Lounge around at home, if possible, assign household tasks to someone else, and try to avoid attending social functions. The whole idea is to let your body restore and regenerate.

PAMPER YOURSELF

While you're cleansing your inside with detoxing foods and juices, it's the ideal time to cleanse and pamper your outside, too.

Drink like a fish during your detox... but make it nothing but juice, water and herbal tea.

DRY BODY BRUSHING AND AN EPSOM SALTS BATH

Dry body brushing is a stimulating therapy. It's a great detoxing treatment because it helps rid the skin of dry, dead cells and improves blood and lymph circulation. That means it helps your body dispose of some of the internal toxins being mobilised by your detox program.

You'll need a natural bristle brush or a hemp mitt. Undress then, on dry skin, use long, upward sweeping movements, starting at your feet and working up your legs and across your hips and bottom (the strokes should be towards your heart). From there, run the brush in a clockwise motion over your stomach then gently rub over your decolletage area and down your arms to your fingers.

Don't brush your breasts, face or throat, and be careful not to rub your skin too hard. Rough scrubbing can break tiny capillaries, not to mention leave you red and raw.

After you've finished dry brushing you can have shower, or you may want to run a warm bath and put in one to two cups of Epsom salts – available from chemists or supermarkets. These contain magnesium, a mineral required for nearly all the body's cellular activity, and is especially important to healthy muscle function.

An Epsom salts bath will stimulate lymph drainage and draw toxins out through the pores on the skin. For maximum detoxing benefits, soak about 20 minutes. Afterwards, it is recommended that you drink plenty of water and relax for an hour, as an Epsom salts bath can be quite draining.

For best results, take an Epsom salts bath every three days during a detox program. However, you shouldn't have one if you suffer from a skin condition, or have any cuts.

AROMATHERAPY

There are few more luxurious ways to help you detox, as well as stimulate your senses, revive your soul and heal your mind and body, than aromatherapy.

While many people might think of aromatherapy simply as a form of treatment that involves pleasant-smelling oils, it is much more than that. The plant-extracted essential oils really do have therapeutic effects. They also can be dangerous if used incorrectly or in the wrong amounts, so always follow the instructions.

The easiest ways to use aromatherapy oils are in an oil burner or a bath. Using an oil burner is an ideal accompaniment to any relaxation or meditation that you may perform during your detox. Fill the oil-burner dish with water and light the candle. Add about five drops of essential oil to the water (some oils are not suitable for a burner, so check the label before use), and within minutes the aroma from the heated oil will gradually permeate the room.

An aromatherapy bath can feel like a luxurious treat while acting as a great tonic for the body, and the steam from the bath carries more aroma molecules to your nose than when you burn them.

The best way to use essential oils in the bath is to add them a drop at a time, using no more than six to eight drops in a full bath. Don't add more if you can't smell them after a while; they're still working. Also, don't have the water too hot or you may feel light-headed. For the same reason, saunas and steam rooms are not recommended during a detox, although they can be helpful later to keep the body healthy by helping to eliminate toxins.

As you rest in the bath your muscles relax and release lactic acid; your pores open and release toxins in the form of sweat; and your digestive system is stimulated by the heat of the bath. Your open pores allow the essential oil to penetrate your skin more readily. Try one of the essential oil blends (page 15), for a relaxing detox bath.

OTHER HYDROTHERAPY TREATMENTS

There are a number of ways to benefit from the power of water other than soaking in it.

Yes, hydrotherapy does include such treatments as an aromatherapy bath, but it can also be more specifically used as a hot and/or cold sitz bath, a hot and/or cold foot bath or a fomentation (the applation of warm liquid to the skin).

The idea is that the body doesn't respond to the water itself, but to the variations in the water temperature – heat dilates the vessels, increases the blood flow and relaxes the nerves and tissues while cold constricts the vessels, reduces the blood flow and stimulates the nerves and tissues.

While a sitz bath requires two tubs, and is too difficult to do at home (although you may want to take the treatment at a salon), a hot and cold foot bath is easy to perform.

You'll need one bucket or bowl of hot water (40°C) and another filled with cold tap water. Place your feet in the hot water first. Wiggle your toes and gently twist your ankles for three minutes while your feet are in the water. Then put your feet into the cold water for one minute. Repeat twice, finishing with the cold water. Then dry your feet briskly. This treatment is good for stimulating circulation.

A fomentation is a gentle heat treatment used to improve blood circulation and waste elimination. It can decrease pain, increase mobility and reduce inflammation of joints or muscles. Fomentations can also be used over the region of various body organs, such as the liver, lungs, kidneys, stomach and lower abdominal area, to speed up the removal of waste products from the tissues.

ESSENTIAL OIL BATH BLENDS

- To soothe aching muscles, boost the immune and digestive systems and bring a sense of peace and harmony, mix three drops of lavender, two drops of geranium and one drop of clary sage into bath.
- To boost the immune system and bring clarity to the mind, mix two drops of eucalyptus, two drops of tea tree, two drops of geranium and one drop of clary sage into bath.
- To quiet a busy brain, mix one drop of chamomile, two drops of lavender, two drops of bergamot and one drop of sandalwood into bath.

You'll need 10 towels, a hot-water bottle and, ideally, someone to help lay the towels over you if the area is hard to reach.

Begin by filling the hot-water bottle and wrapping it in one towel; put it aside for a moment. Make sure you're positioned comfortably, perhaps on the floor with pillows to support your body.

Now, place eight layers of towels over the area you wish to be treated. Place the towel-wrapped hot-water bottle on top for three minutes. Remove the hot-water bottle and towels, then take a wet towel (soaked in cold water and wrung out so it doesn't drip) and place it on the area you are treating for one minute. Repeat this procedure two more times, finishing with the cold towel.

Do not continue if the pain increases, and never do more than two treatments a day.

PAMPERING DURING DETOX

Stress is a major contributor to a toxic state, but pampering and relaxation techniques can allow our body to release tension and anxiety.

Reflexology, full-body massages and facials can all help relax the nervous system and speed the elimination of stress-induced toxins from the body. And not only that, they feel great, too.

REFLEXOLOGY

Reflexology is said to stimulate our natural healing abilities and balance and energise our body's systems.

Our feet are considered miniature maps of our bodies, and reflexologists believe that poor diet, stress, lack of exercise and illness can cause congestion in the feet, resulting in deposits of crystalline-like lumps around the nerve endings. These lumps are broken down during treatment by deep finger massage of the feet.

To help them navigate the feet – and the body – reflexologists use a chart that shows which areas and points of the feet correspond to other parts of the body, such as the liver or the sinuses. They then look for tender spots, where they apply pressure to break down any crystalline deposits. These are then eliminated from the body through the bloodstream.

Reflexologists believe that this has a flow-on effect in the body – with the deposits eliminated, the body part they correspond to can become more healthy.

To be your own reflexologist, start with a bath, shower or even a foot soak (try adding a disinfecting essential oil such as lime or lemon). Gently dry your feet, making sure you dry between your toes.

Start with the right foot and use your thumb to 'walk' in a straight line along the outside edge of the foot. With each movement of the thumb, press down into the foot – not so that you experience pain, but just deep enough to feel a release of tension in the foot. Next, walk the thumb over the ball of the foot in rows until you have covered the area. Then, walk the thumb along the left, middle and right side of each toe.

If you notice any tender spots while you are doing this, don't panic – while they could indicate that you may have some congestion in the corresponding body part, they will become less and less tender if you continue to practice reflexology.

Many people find the arch to be the most tender part of the foot, and this may be particularly true during a detox. Reflexologists claim the arch has many points that correspond to the elimination organs (the lungs, kidneys and bowel). Working on the arch also helps improve circulation, which, in turn, helps the body to remove wastes and toxins more effectively.

Two drops of cedarwood or eucalyptus essential oil mixed into 4ml of a carrier oil, such as almond oil, and rubbed into your feet while you perform your reflexology treatment will help flush the kidneys and keep your feet fresh.

SOME ESSENTIAL OILS AND THEIR USES

Bergamot	relieves stress, depression and fatigue
Cedarwood	comforting, helps calm the nerves
Chamomile	calms the nerves
Clary sage	helps relieve stress, tension and mild anxiety
Eucalyptus	can help relieve cold and flu symptoms
Fennel	detoxifying, good for digestive problems, tiredness
Frankincense	helps bring comfort
Geranium	helps calm the nerves, relieves anxiety and tension
Grapefruit	detoxifying, uplifting
Ginger	warming and stimulating
Juniper	calming and detoxifying
Lavender	helps relieve insomnia, nervous tension and headache
Lemon	helps relieve cold symptoms
Lime	refreshing and reviving
Mandarin	a diuretic, also has sedative properties
Myrrh	has anti-inflammatory properties
Orange	helps relieve stress and tension
Peppermint	clears the head, good for fatigue
Rosemary	uplifting and focusing
Sandalwood	warming and grounding
Tea tree	cleansing, uplifting and refreshing
Ylang ylang	a sedative, calms the nerves

NOTE All essential oils must be used with caution. Some oils should be avoided by people with certain medical conditions or skin sensitivities, and by those who are pregnant. If you are unsure whether you can use essential oils, it is important to first talk to a qualified naturopathic practitioner or GP. Never take essential oils internally.

MASSAGE

For a pleasurable way to knead toxins from the tissues, promote lymph drainage, stimulate glandular secretions and calm the nervous system, try one of the many types of massage. It can relieve tension, help improve the immune system, tone the skin and muscles, and improve the appearance of skin, especially in areas prone to cellulite.

Book a treatment before you start your detox program, but take time to consider which style of massage will suit you best.

You may find a gentle Swedish massage is as much as you feel up to. Or, maybe a deeper therapy, such as remedial massage, is just what you need to get circulation going. Other options include shiatsu massage, which involves stretching, manipulation and acupressure and can be quite painful (but effective), and kahuna massage, an energetic process that helps connect body and soul.

You can also massage yourself – or at least the parts you can reach. All massage strokes should be towards your heart, pushing the blood around your body in conjunction with the circulation, not against it. Self-massage isn't quite as relaxing as having someone else do it for you, though.

BREATHING

If you are what you eat, you're also a product of how you breathe. In fact, learning to breathe properly is an essential part of any self-healing detox program. If the body does not expel sufficient carbon dioxide, toxins build up.

Deep, rhythmic breathing enhances oxygenation of the blood and tissues, and switches the nervous system into the healing mode. By contrast, shallow, overbreathing can put you in a state of anxiety that can lead to ill health.

Try this simple breathing exercise to de-stress and recharge: sit comfortably or lie down. Place your hands gently on your stomach, with your fingertips touching. Close your eyes and take a few normal breaths while you say the word "calm" in your mind.

Now, breathe in through your nose, very slowly, to a count of four. As you inhale, push your belly up and out. Hold your breath for five counts, then gently exhale through your mouth to a count of eight. Repeat this process up to 10 times.

FACIALS

It's day two of your detox and you look like a teenager again. Don't worry. Breaking out during a cleansing program is normal. And once you've detoxed your body, skin problems should subside. To help your skin clear up, and to add extra relaxation to your detox regime, consider having a facial.

If you decide to visit a salon, make sure you choose somewhere with a relaxing atmosphere. Ask what the treatment includes before you book to make sure it will fit in with your regime.

A head or shoulder massage or being left alone with a mask on for 15 minutes are both pluses because they help you relax and give you time for reflection.

If you'd prefer to treat yourself at home, stock up on some of your favourite cleanser, mask and moisturiser products before you start your detox. Or, for a natural treatment, raid the pantry, the kitchen is the ideal place for facial ingredients – you can't go past honey, natural yogurt or oatmeal. Also try your local chemist or health-food store for supplies. These are ideal places to seek out chemical-free beauty products.

A facial sauna is a good way to prepare your face for facial masks. (You should not use facial saunas if you have sensitive skin, are pregnant or suffer from asthma.) Give these facial saunas a try.

Fill a large glass bowl with 1 litre (4 cups) of near boiling water; add ingredients according to your skin type (page 17). Place a towel over your head and hold it over the bowl from a distance of about 30cm for a period of about 2 minutes. Close your eyes and breathe normally;

> Learning to breathe properly is an essential part of any self-healing detox program.

allow the steam to open your pores. Remove your face from the sauna; pat face with a warm face washer. Normal skin: add 6 drops mandarin essential oil and 2 tablespoons loose lavender tea to water. Oily skin: add 6 drops eucalyptus essential oil and 2 tablespoons loose lemon tea to water. Dry skin: add 6 drops rose essential oil and 2 tablespoons loose chamomile tea to water.

Ideally, perform home treatments when you are alone and have some private time and space – and don't forget to take the phone off the hook. It's all about self-pampering; an indulgence to build into your life, even after you finish your detox program.

POSSIBLE SIDE EFFECTS OF DETOXING

Unfair as it may seem, some people get next to no detoxing symptoms. However, most people will notice some annoying side effects, and these will also vary greatly from person to person.

Detoxing symptoms commonly include headaches, lower back pain, dry mouth, coated tongue, bad breath, skin rashes, nausea, body odour, weakness, fatigue, abdominal gas and rumblings, palpitations, mucous discharges, irritability, boredom, anxiety, emotional upset, joint and muscular aches and pains, cold feet and hands, vivid dreams, sleeplessness and more. As well, existing health problems, such as arthritis, may seem to worsen initially, and the effects of old injuries may also become evident.

The first three or four days is the most common time for reactions and withdrawal symptoms to occur, so it's naturally the most difficult time. But if you find you can put up with mild-to-moderate side effects, don't get discouraged – keep going. However, as previously advised, if you feel light-headed or dizzy, have a level of headache or muscle pain you rate as severe, or develop a rash you don't think is normal, stop the detox program immediately and see your doctor. Otherwise, any unpleasant side effects will eventually settle down.

HOMEMADE FACIALS

YOGURT & HONEY CLEANSER

1 tablespoon honey
¼ cup (70g) natural yogurt
rose essential oil

Combine honey and yogurt in small bowl. Add a few drops of essential oil; mix well. Apply generously to damp face; massage into skin in an upward circular motion, avoiding eye area. Remove using warm face washer. Rinse with warm water; pat dry.
TIP Store cleanser in a screw-top jar in the refrigerator for one week.

KIWI FRUIT & LIME TONER

2 medium kiwi fruit (170g), peeled, chopped coarsely
⅓ cup (80ml) fresh lime juice

Using a food processor, process kiwi fruit until almost smooth; transfer to small bowl, add lime juice, mix well. Place a new piece of muslin, in a single layer, in small strainer over a bowl. Pour fruit mixture over muslin; using a rubber spatula, gently push liquid through cloth. Discard pulp and seeds. Using a cotton ball, apply toner to face after cleansing, avoiding eye area. Rinse with cool water; pat dry.
TIP Store toner in a screw-top jar in refrigerator for one week.

ALMOND & PAPAYA FACIAL SCRUB

¼ cup (40g) blanched almonds
⅓ cup (40g) oat bran
1 teaspoon sweet almond oil
2 tablespoons pureed papaya flesh
1 tablespoon natural yogurt
2 tablespoons honey

Using a food processor, process almonds until they resemble fine breadcrumbs; transfer to small bowl. Add remaining ingredients, mix well. Apply small amount of scrub to damp cleansed face. Gently rub in a circular motion over face concentrating on problem areas, avoid eye area. Rinse face with warm water; pat dry.
TIP Store scrub in a screw-top jar in refrigerator for one week.

MOISTURISING APRICOT & ALMOND MASK

½ cup (75g) dried apricots
1 cup (250ml) hot water
1 tablespoon skim milk powder
2 tablespoons sweet almond oil
1 tablespoon hot water, extra

Combine apricots and the water in small bowl; soak for 20 minutes or until apricots are softened. Drain. Using a food processor, process apricots with remaining ingredients until smooth. Apply mask, using a small spatula, to clean, dry face, avoiding eye and lip area. Relax for 15 minutes. Remove mask with a warm face washer; rinse and pat dry.

BANANA & AVOCADO MASK

¼ medium ripe banana (50g)
¼ medium ripe avocado (50g)
1 teaspoon honey
3 teaspoons cornflour

Using a fork, mash banana and avocado in a small bowl until almost smooth. Push mixture through a small sieve using the back of a spoon into a small bowl. Add honey and cornflour; mix well. Apply mask, using a small spatula, to a clean, dry face, avoiding eye and lip area. Relax for 15 minutes. Remove mask with a warm face washer; rinse and pat dry.

CUCUMBER, STRAWBERRY & GRAPE COOLING MASK

20 small seedless red grapes (65g)
½ medium cucumber (85g), deseeded, chopped coarsely
3 strawberries (75g), halved
1 tablespoon natural yogurt
½ teaspoon honey

Using a food processor, process grapes, cucumber and strawberry until combined. Place a large, new piece of muslin, folded in quarters, in small bowl. Spoon mixture into centre of cloth; gather corners of cloth and twist to squeeze liquid from mixture into bowl; discard liquid. Place fruit pulp into cleaned small bowl. Add yogurt and honey; mix well. Apply mask, using a small spatula, to a clean, dry face, avoiding eye and lip area. Relax for 15 minutes. Gently remove mask with a warm face washer; rinse with warm water and pat dry.

HERBAL TEAS

Herbal teas are no longer the brew of choice only for health fanatics or those who are vehemently anti-caffeine. These calming, reviving and healing teas have become more mainstream as an ever-increasing number of people discover their exotic flavours and soothing medicinal qualities. The result is that it is easier than ever to order a herbal tea at a chic cafe, or to buy some – not just at specialised tea shops or health-food stores, but also in supermarkets.

There are literally hundreds of different blends you can experiment with – if you buy your tea from a specialist shop, ask the staff to suggest something to suit your tastes and needs. Meanwhile, here are a few suggestions to get you started:

- Rosehip tea gives you a boost of vitamin C, which can help strengthen your immune system and is vital for anti-ageing.
- Raspberry tea is also a good source of vitamin C. It can be used as a blood purifier and tonic as well as help control diarrhoea. It can also help in reducing painful menstruation.
- Strawberry leaf tea is believed to help soothe stomach troubles and eczema.
- Thyme tea can help improve your immune system as well as promote perspiration.
- Peppermint tea can stimulate digestion after dinner
- Camomile tea helps soothe the stomach and nerves to prepare for a good night's sleep.
- Dandelion tea is an effective diuretic that can also help improve liver function.
- Lemon balm tea can help lift your spirits.
- Teas containing chaparral, schisandra and St Mary's thistle are all potent ways to treat toxic poisoning of the body. Therefore, they're a great detox tool.

Look for these herbs in tea blends and, for maximum detoxing properties, choose high quality loose-leaf teas, not tea bags. You need to steep the tea in boiling water for at least three minutes to gain benefits from its healing properties. Buying yourself a beautiful teapot, or cup and saucer, can help turn brewing a pot of herbal tea into a special ritual.

DETOXING YOUR EMOTIONS

For a detox to work on all aspects of your life, you need to do more than cleanse your body... you need to detox your emotions. Holistic healers believe that old resentments can burden your body and deplete your energy and, surprisingly, this idea is slowly becoming more accepted by practioners of traditional medicine.

That's because there is increasing evidence that emotions create chemical reactions in the body, and that these substances, which have the potential to cause health problems later, can be stored in muscles and organs. This area of 'emotional' science is called neuroscience or 'bodymind' medicine. While much more research is needed into the field, there is no doubt that holding onto anger, resentment, frustration or envy can wear down your mind and body. If nothing else, you will regularly feel fatigued and have a diminished capacity to enjoy your everyday life.

Emotional detoxing means not only addressing these old 'wounds', but also any harmful thought patterns and habits that lead to fear and anxiety – both of which can impact on your health. So take some time during your detox program to sit quietly and think about what negative emotions you regularly feel, or what negative thoughts consistently run through your mind. You may decide that you need to learn to laugh more, to be more patient with others – or yourself – to talk about your emotions rather than bottle them up – or even to give up being a perfectionist.

At the same time, you may want to let go of old hurts or disappointments that prevent you being healthy and happy. It may be a simple matter of forgiving others – or yourself – for what is in the past, or simply accepting something the way it is. A simple ceremony, such as burning a letter in which you have written the feelings or experiences you want to shed, or spending 20 minutes a day during detox in quiet meditation, may be all the emotional medicine you need.

However, if you discover some deep emotional issues that you think you need help in dealing with, seek the support of a therapist or counsellor after your detox to help you achieve a state of wellness and fulfilment. Remember, one of the aims of a detox is to learn how to look after yourself using healthy food, regular exercise and self-pampering. Practising positive self-talk and addressing toxic emotions should be part of your resolve to stay well.

EATING OUT DURING DETOX

If you choose to go to a restaurant while you're detoxing, you probably possess a will of iron. But if you really want to eat out, here are some tips to help you avoid falling off the detox wagon.

First, tell your dining companions that you are on a detox program rather than make excuses about why you're avoiding the wine, or passing on the tiramisu. Second, tell the waiter that you don't want butter, oil or salt added to your food. Choose a salad, without any dressing, or a vegetarian entree or main. And don't be afraid to ask how the meals have been prepared, or to request that certain ingredients be omitted. Bottled water is a good drink choice, but ask if the restaurant will prepare you a fresh juice. Enjoy the company of friends, rather than concentrating on the food, and you'll find eating out is not quite so daunting.

COMING OUT OF DETOX

It's important to ease your body out of a detox program. That's why we've included a 'day after' menu in the one-week and two-week detoxes. After you've gone through these menus, continue on the straight and narrow with a healthy, varied diet based on the key foods found in the detoxing menus. Try not to over-exert yourself and, if possible, don't rush straight back to anything that will cause you stress. Don't be surprised if you feel different emotionally as well as physically – you've cleared out toxins that have been weighing down your body and mind.

AFTER DETOX

In a perfect world, everyone who goes on a detox would continue to live a lifestyle that was so healthy they'd never need to detox again. But we live in the real world, with all its physical, mental and emotional challenges and temptations. Aim to take some of the healthy dietary habits you have learned during detox into our everyday life and add relaxation and exercise programs that keep your body and mind healthy. Stock your pantry and fridge with the natural, energy-giving foods you enjoyed on your detox. Buy in-season fruit and vegetables to get maximum nutritional benefit and, if possible, buy organic. Remember to build pampering and healing routines into your daily life, and don't forget to spend some time each day detoxing negative emotions.

After your detox, we strongly recommend you begin and maintain a regular exercise program. Exercise improves circulation, so your body can carry oxygen and expel wastes more effectively; enhances your sense of wellbeing; helps control your appetite and your weight; and de-stresses your body. Without exercise the adrenalin you produce in a hyperactive state has no outlet and can harm muscles, joints and organs. While you're detoxing, make a plan to learn Pilates, yoga, tai chi or other gentle forms of exercise that treat the body and the mind. Other ideas for fun exercise include hiking, abseiling, trampolining, rollerblading, skiing, cycling and dancing.

> Ideally, everyone who goes on a detox would continue to live an idyllic lifestyle that was so healthy they'd never need to detox again.

MORE WAYS TO REDUCE TOXIC OVERLOAD

- Avoid using plastics in food preparation. Store food in glass containers and use greaseproof paper instead of plastic wrap. Use stainless steel, glass or earthenware in the kitchen.
- Keep chemicals in and around your house, garden and car to a minimum.
- Avoid anything that is bleached with chlorine, including coffee filter paper and tea bags that don't say they're unbleached.
- Avoid walking in polluted parts of the city, and wear a mask if you cycle in the city.
- Use a water filter to remove chlorine, or buy pure bottled water.
- Use medication, including painkillers, only if absolutely necessary.
- If you must drink, choose a spirit.
- Try not to sit in front of a computer for more than five hours a day. Research suggests even low-level radiation for long periods may place the body under toxic stress. Turn off your computer when you're not using it. Get away from it completely by going for a walk at lunchtime.
- Invest in houseplants such as ferns, palms and chrysanthemums which help reduce levels of chemicals. Take a small pot plant to work to help reduce pollutants from computers and printers.
- Eat enzyme-rich foods, such as pineapple and sprouted foods, to encourage proper digestion and elimination.

menu plans

one-day mono-food detox

This can be a good way to introduce yourself to the idea of detox. It's simple: you just eat one type of raw fruit or vegetable for the entire day. The food most commonly chosen is grapes, but you may also like to consider apples, pears, carrots or even papaya. Make sure you eat lightly the night before your one-day detox, and get plenty of rest.

BREAKFAST
Hot lemon water *page 35*
Grapes or grape juice
(or your chosen fruit
or vegetable)

MORNING TEA
Grapes or grape juice
(or your chosen fruit or
vegetable)
Filtered water

LUNCH
Grapes or grape juice
(or your chosen fruit or
vegetable)
Filtered water

AFTERNOON TEA
Grapes or grape juice
(or your chosen fruit or
vegetable)
Herbal tea *page 18*

DINNER
Grapes or grape juice
(or your chosen fruit or
vegetable)
Filtered water or herbal tea
page 18

Don't go mad the next day – ease out of your detox gently with a light, healthy diet.

one-weekend detox

THE NIGHT BEFORE
DINNER
Mixed bean salad *page 69*

DAY ONE
BREAKFAST
Hot lemon water *page 35*
Peach, apple and
strawberry juice *page 24*
Papaya with passionfruit
and lime *page 43*

MORNING TEA
Watermelon and mint
juice *page 27*

LUNCH
Lamb's lettuce salad with
pecans and orange *page 60*

AFTERNOON TEA
Watercress, beetroot
and celery juice
page 24

DINNER
Asian broth *page 59*

DAY TWO
BREAKFAST
Hot lemon water *page 35*
Orange and ginger juice
page 26
Mango cheeks with lime
wedges *page 47*

MORNING TEA
Pineapple, orange and
strawberry juice *page 27*

LUNCH
Green vegetable salad with
american mustard dressing
page 73

AFTERNOON TEA
Ginger tea *page 37*

DINNER
Stir-fried asian greens with
tofu *page 92*

NOTE Juices should be no larger than 250ml. You should always rinse your mouth or clean your teeth after drinking citrus juices as they're acid and could damage your teeth enamel.

seven-day detox

THE DAY BEFORE

BREAKFAST
Apple and blueberry
muesli *page 41*

LUNCH
White bean salad *page 69*

DINNER
Vegetable stir-fry served
with steamed brown rice
page 65

DAY ONE

BREAKFAST
Hot lemon water *page 35*
Mixed berry juice
page 26
Four-fruit combo
page 43

MORNING TEA
Watermelon and mint juice
page 27

LUNCH
Orange, fennel and
almond salad *page 91*

AFTERNOON TEA
Beetroot, carrot and
spinach juice *page 27*

DINNER
Roasted cherry tomatoes,
broccoli and pepitas
page 95

DAY TWO

BREAKFAST
Hot lemon water *page 35*
Strawberry and papaya
juice *page 24*
1 banana

MORNING TEA
Mixed berry juice *page 26*

LUNCH
Spinach and courgette
salad with yogurt hummus
page 73

AFTERNOON TEA
Grapes

DINNER
Ratatouille *page 95*

DAY THREE

BREAKFAST
Hot lemon water page 35
Raspberry and peach juice
page 26
1 nectarine

MORNING TEA
Grapes

LUNCH
Greek salad *page 74*

AFTERNOON TEA
Swiss chard, apple and
celery juice *page 28*

DINNER
Black-eyed beans with
sweet potato, shallots
and garlic *page 99*

DAY FOUR

BREAKFAST
Hot lemon water *page 35*
Orange, carrot and ginger
juice *page 32*
Macerated fruits *page 42*

MORNING TEA
Watercress, beetroot and
celery juice *page 24*

LUNCH
Roasted tomato and
pepper soup *page 53*

AFTERNOON TEA
Strawberry, honey and
soy smoothie *page 28*

DINNER
Stir-fried asian greens with
mixed mushrooms served
with steamed brown rice
page 96

DAY FIVE

BREAKFAST
Hot lemon water *page 35*
Mango and grapefruit juice
page 29
Cherries and yogurt
page 47

MORNING TEA
½ mango

LUNCH
Potato and bean salad
with lemon yogurt dressing
page 77

AFTERNOON TEA
Mint tea *page 37*

DINNER
Roasted vegetable stack
page 105

DAY SIX

BREAKFAST
Hot lemon water *page 35*
Peach, apple and
strawberry juice *page 24*
Apple and blueberry muesli
page 41

MORNING TEA
Pineapple, ginger and mint
juice *page 30*

LUNCH
Vegetable soup *page 55*

Lamb's lettuce salad
with pecans and orange
page 60

AFTERNOON TEA
Carrot dip with crudités
page 67

DINNER
Pearl barley salad *page 75*

DAY SEVEN

BREAKFAST
Hot lemon water *page 35*
Pear and ginger juice
page 32
Macerated fruits *page 42*

MORNING TEA
Orange, carrot and ginger
juice *page 33*

LUNCH
Dhal with vegetables
page 101

AFTERNOON TEA
Beetroot, carrot and
spinach juice *page 27*

DINNER
Pan-fried tofu with
vietnamese coleslaw salad
page 79

THE DAY AFTER

BREAKFAST
Apple and blueberry
muesli *page 41*

LUNCH
Goat's cheese. salad and
pecan sandwich *page 63*

DINNER
Steamed asian bream
page 109

two-week detox

TWO DAYS BEFORE
BREAKFAST
Apple and pear juice
page 28
Apple and blueberry
muesli *page 41*

LUNCH
Open rye sandwich
page 65

DINNER
Grilled fish fillet with gai larn
page 111

ONE DAY BEFORE
BREAKFAST
Pear and ginger juice
page 32
Apple and blueberry
muesli *page 41*

LUNCH
Asparagus caesar salad
page 71

DINNER
Vegetable and white bean
stew *page 111*

DAY ONE
BREAKFAST
Hot lemon water
page 35
Apple and celery juice
page 29
Banana with passionfruit
yogurt *page 43*

MORNING TEA
Pineapple, ginger and mint
juice *page 30*

LUNCH
Greek salad *page 74*

AFTERNOON TEA
Lemongrass and kaffir
lime tea *page 36*

DINNER
Brown rice with
vegetables and tahini
dressing *page 99*

DAY TWO
BREAKFAST
Hot lemon water *page 35*
Mandarin juice *page 30*
Apple and pear compote
with dates *page 38*

MORNING TEA
Mint tea *page 37*

LUNCH
Cos, mangetout and roast
celeriac salad *page 77*

AFTERNOON TEA
Beetroot, carrot and
spinach juice *page 27*

DINNER
Brown rice pilaf *page 103*

DAY THREE
BREAKFAST
Hot lemon water *page 35*
Ginger, orange and
pineapple juice *page 30*
Kiwi fruit, lychee and lime
salad *page 46*

MORNING TEA
Grapes

LUNCH
Chickpea, watercress
and pepper salad
page 81

AFTERNOON TEA
Hummus with crudités
page 67

DINNER
Baked potato with
guacamole *page 96*

DAY FOUR
BREAKFAST
Hot lemon water *page 35*
Grapefruit and blood
orange juice *page 31*
1 banana

MORNING TEA
Melon slices (one type)

LUNCH
Potato and asparagus
salad with yogurt and mint
dressing *page 81*

AFTERNOON TEA
Swiss chard, apple and
celery juice *page 28*

DINNER
Leek, goat's cheese
and brown lentil bake
page 101

DAY FIVE
BREAKFAST
Hot lemon water *page 35*
Kiwi fruit and green grape
juice *page 31*
Figs and sheep's milk
yogurt and honey *page 45*

MORNING TEA
Pineapple, orange and
strawberry juice *page 27*

LUNCH
Borlotti bean, brown
rice and almond salad
page 83

AFTERNOON TEA
Cardamom and chamomile
tea *page 36*

DINNER
Roasted plum tomatoes
with barley salad *page 83*

DAY SIX
BREAKFAST
Hot lemon water *page 35*
Apple and pear juice
page 28
Banana with passionfruit
page 43

MORNING TEA
Strawberry, honey and
soy smoothie *page 28*

LUNCH
Pear, spinach, walnut
and celery salad *page 75*

AFTERNOON TEA
Beetroot dip with
crudités *page 66*

DINNER
Roasted root vegetables
with yogurt *page 103*

DAY SEVEN
BREAKFAST
Hot lemon water
page 35
Orange, carrot and celery
juice *page 32*
Apple and pear compote
with dates *page 38*

MORNING TEA
Tangelo and ginger juice
page 31

LUNCH
Leek and potato soup
page 55

AFTERNOON TEA
Cinnamon and orange
tea *page 37*

DINNER
Brown rice with
vegetables and tahini
dressing *page 99*

DAY EIGHT
BREAKFAST
Hot lemon water
page 35
Mandarin juice *page 30*
1 pear

MORNING TEA
1 custard apple

LUNCH
Aubergine with salsa fresca
page 97

AFTERNOON TEA
Raita with crudités
page 66

DINNER
Thai soya bean salad with
grapes and pink grapefruit
page 87

DAY NINE
BREAKFAST
Hot lemon water *page 35*
Ginger, orange and
pineapple juice *page 30*
Lychees with passionfruit
page 45

MORNING TEA
Blood plums with honey and
cardamom yogurt *page 49*

LUNCH
Soba salad with seaweed,
ginger and vegetables
page 85

AFTERNOON TEA
Mint tea *page 37*

DINNER
Grilled asparagus with
warm tomato dressing
page 87

DAY TEN
BREAKFAST
Hot lemon water *page 35*
Pear and grape juice
page 29
Stewed prunes with orange
page 49

MORNING TEA
Lemongrass and kaffir
lime tea *page 36*

LUNCH
Pumpkin and sweet potato
soup *page 53*

AFTERNOON TEA
Carrot dip with crudités
page 67

DINNER
Baked beetroot salad with
cannellini beans, feta and
mint *page 89*

DAY ELEVEN
BREAKFAST
Hot lemon water *page 35*
Orange, carrot and celery
juice *page 33*
Mango cheeks with lime
wedges *page 47*

MORNING TEA
1 banana

LUNCH
Roasted pumpkin, pecan
and feta salad *page 91*

AFTERNOON TEA
Ginger tea *page 37*

DINNER
Stir-fried asian greens with
mushrooms *page 96*

DAY TWELVE
BREAKFAST
Hot lemon water *page 35*
Orange, mango and
strawberry juice *page 32*
1 cup mixed berries

MORNING TEA
Watercress, beetroot and
celery juice *page 24*

LUNCH
Vegetable and soba soup
page 59

AFTERNOON TEA
Beetroot dip with crudités
page 66

DINNER
Chickpea patties with
tomato and cucumber
salad *page 105*

DAY THIRTEEN
BREAKFAST
Hot lemon water *page 35*
Orange, carrot and ginger
juice *page 33*
Watermelon slices

MORNING TEA
Cinnamon and orange tea
page 36

LUNCH
Dhal with vegetables
page 101

AFTERNOON TEA
Carrot, ginger and swiss
chard juice *page 33*

DINNER
Stir-fried tofu with
vegetables and lemongrass
page 97

DAY FOURTEEN
BREAKFAST
Hot lemon water *page 35*
Apple and blueberry muesli
page 41
Melon slices

MORNING TEA
Banana soy smoothie
page 33

LUNCH
Tomato and avocado salad
with tofu pesto *page 74*

AFTERNOON TEA
Hummus with crudités
page 67

DINNER
Lentil and vegetable soup
page 57

THE DAY AFTER
BREAKFAST
Apple and blueberry muesli
page 41

LUNCH
Vegetable wrap *page 63*

DINNER
Oven-roasted ratatouille
with almond gremolata
page 107

TWO DAYS AFTER
BREAKFAST
Porridge with poached
pears and blueberries
page 41

LUNCH
Vegetable soup *page 55*
Cos, mangetout and
roast celeriac salad
page 77

DINNER
Poached fish with herb
salad *page 109*

juices and drinks

peach, apple and strawberry juice

preparation time 5 minutes
serves 1

**1 medium apple (150g),
cut into wedges
1 medium peach (150g),
cut into wedges
2 strawberries (40g)**

1 Push ingredients through juice extractor into glass; stir to combine.
TIP We used a green apple, but you can use the colour of your choice.

per serving 0.3g total fat (0g saturated fat); 24.3g carbohydrate 451kJ (108 cal); 2.2g protein; 5.1g fibre

watercress, beetroot and celery juice

preparation time 5 minutes
serves 1

**1 trimmed celery stalk (100g),
chopped coarsely
3 baby beetroots (75g),
cut into wedges
50g watercress, trimmed
½ cup (125ml) water**

1 Push celery, beetroot and watercress through juice extractor into glass. Stir in the water.

per serving 0.4g total fat; (0g saturated fat); 8.9g carbohydrate; 222kJ (53 cal); 3.5g protein; 6g fibre

strawberry and papaya juice

preparation time 5 minutes
serves 1

**4 strawberries (80g)
80g papaya
½ cup (125ml) water**

1 Blend or process ingredients until smooth.
TIP For something refreshing, freeze the juice until almost set then scrape with a fork for a granita-like snack. We used the red-fleshed Hawaiian or Fijian variety of papaya in this recipe.

per serving 0.2g total fat; (0g saturated fat); 7.7g carbohydrate; 163kJ (39 cal); 1.7g protein; 3.6g fibre

orange and ginger juice

preparation time 5 minutes
serves 1

3 medium oranges (720g)
2cm piece fresh ginger
(10g), grated

1 Juice oranges on citrus squeezer; pour into glass.
2 Stir in ginger.

per serving 0.6g total fat;
(0g saturated fat); 40.9g
carbohydrate; 807kJ (193 cal);
5.2g protein; 10.5g fibre

raspberry and peach juice

preparation time 5 minutes
serves 1

1 large peach (220g), chopped
coarsely
¼ cup (35g) raspberries
½ cup (125ml) water

1 Blend or process peach and raspberry until smooth; pour into glass.
2 Stir in the water.

per serving 0.3g total fat;
(0g saturated fat); 14.1g
carbohydrate; 301kJ (72 cal);
2.1g protein; 4.5g fibre

mixed berry juice

preparation time 5 minutes
serves 1

3 strawberries (60g)
¼ cup (40g) blueberries
¼ cup (35g) raspberries
⅓ cup (80ml) water

1 Blend or process ingredients until smooth; pour into glass.
TIP For something refreshing, freeze the juice until almost set then scrape with a fork for a granita-like snack.

per serving 0.2g total fat
(0g saturated fat); 8.2g carbohydrate;
184kJ (44 cal); 1.7g protein;
3.9g fibre

watermelon and mint juice

preparation time 5 minutes
serves 1

450g watermelon
4 fresh mint leaves

1 Blend or process ingredients until smooth; pour into glass.

per serving 0.6g total fat (0g saturated fat); 14.5g carbohydrate; 280kJ (67 cal); 0.9g protein; 1.9g fibre

pineapple, orange and strawberry juice

preparation time 5 minutes
serves 1

1 small orange (180g), peeled, quartered
150g pineapple, chopped coarsely
2 strawberries (40g)
¼ cup (60ml) water

1 Push orange, pineapple and strawberries through juice extractor into glass; stir in the water.

per serving 0.3g total fat (0g saturated fat); 23.2g carbohydrate; 468kJ (112 cal); 3.5g protein; 6.6g fibre

beetroot, carrot and spinach juice

preparation time 5 minutes
serves 1

1 small beetroot (100g), cut into wedges
1 small carrot (70g), chopped coarsely
20g baby spinach leaves
½ cup (125ml) water

1 Push beetroot, carrot and spinach through juice extractor into glass. Stir in the water.

per serving 0.2g total fat (0g saturated fat); 11.2g carbohydrate; 238kJ (57 cal); 2.7g protein; 5.3g fibre

strawberry, honey and soy smoothie

preparation time 5 minutes
serves 1

6 strawberries (120g)
½ cup (125ml) soy milk
1 teaspoon honey

1 Blend or process ingredients until smooth; pour into glass.

per serving 3.6g total fat (0.4g saturated fat); 14.4g carbohydrate; 472kJ (113 cal); 6.2g protein; 3.2g fibre

apple and pear juice

preparation time 5 minutes
serves 1

1 medium apple (150g),
cut into wedges
1 medium pear (230g),
cut into wedges

1 Push ingredients through juice extractor into glass; stir to combine. *TIP We used a green apple in this recipe, but you can use the colour of your choice.*

per serving 0.4g total fat (0g saturated fat); 51.3g carbohydrate; 853kJ (204 cal); 1.1g protein; 9g fibre

swiss chard, apple and celery juice

preparation time 5 minutes
serves 1

1 trimmed swiss chard leaf (80g),
chopped coarsely
1 large apple (200g), cut into
wedges
1 trimmed celery stalk (100g),
chopped coarsely

1 Push ingredients through juice extractor into glass; stir to combine. *TIP We used a green apple in this recipe, but you can use the colour of your choice.*

per serving 0.5g total fat (0g saturated fat); 24.6g carbohydrate; 460kJ (110 cal); 2.4g protein; 7.8g fibre

mango and grapefruit juice

preparation time 5 minutes
serves 1

1 small grapefruit (350g)
1 small mango (300g), chopped
coarsely
¼ cup (60ml) water

1   Juice grapefruit on citrus squeezer; pour into glass.
2   Blend or process mango and the water until smooth. Transfer to same glass; stir to combine.

per serving 0.9g total fat
(0g saturated fat); 37.8g carbohydrate
757kJ (181 cal) 4.2g protein 4.6g
fibre

apple and celery juice

preparation time 5 minutes
serves 1

2 small apples (260g), cut into
wedges
1 trimmed celery stalk (100g),
chopped coarsely

1   Push ingredients through juice extractor into glass; stir to combine.
TIP We used green apples in this recipe, but you can use the colour of your choice.

per serving 0.4g total fat (0g
saturated fat); 34.7g carbohydrate
598kJ (143 cal); 1.4g protein;
7g fibre

pear and grape juice

preparation time 5 minutes
serves 1

1 medium pear (230g),
cut into wedges
175g seedless red grapes

1   Push ingredients through juice extractor into glass; stir to combine.

per serving 0.4g total fat (0g
saturated fat); 55.6g carbohydrate;
953kJ (228 cal); 2.8g protein;
7.3g fibre

pineapple, ginger and mint juice

preparation time 5 minutes
serves 1

400g pineapple, chopped coarsely
1 cup firmly packed fresh mint
leaves
1cm piece fresh ginger (5g)

1 Push ingredients through juice extractor into glass; stir to combine.
TIP You need ½ small pineapple for this recipe.

per serving 0.8g total fat (0.1g saturated fat); 19.1g carbohydrate; 418kJ (100 cal); 3.7g protein; 8.1g fibre

ginger, orange and pineapple juice

preparation time 5 minutes
serves 1

1 medium orange (240g)
200g pineapple, chopped coarsely
2cm piece fresh ginger (10g)

1 Juice orange on citrus squeezer; pour into glass.
2 Blend pineapple and ginger until smooth. Stir into orange juice.
TIP You need ¼ small pineapple for this recipe.

per serving 0.3g total fat (0g saturated fat); 22.2g carbohydrate; 439kJ (105 cal); 2.8g protein; 5.9g fibre

mandarin juice

preparation time 5 minutes
serves 1

3 small mandarins (300g)

1 Juice mandarins on citrus squeezer; pour into glass.

per serving 0.4g total fat (0g saturated fat); 17g carbohydrate; 343kJ (82 cal); 1.9g protein; 4.3g fibre

tangelo and ginger juice

*preparation time 5 minutes
serves 1*

**2 medium tangelos (420g)
2cm piece fresh ginger
(10g), grated**

1 Juice tangelos on citrus
squeezer; pour into glass.
2 Stir in ginger.

*per serving 0.3g total fat (0g
saturated fat); 23.7g carbohydrate;
477kJ (114 cal); 1.9g protein;
6.2g fibre*

kiwi fruit and green grape juice

*preparation time 5 minutes
serves 1*

**3 medium kiwi fruits (255g),
quartered
70g seedless green grapes
¼ cup (60ml) water**

1 Blend or process ingredients
until smooth; pour into glass.

*per serving 0.5g total fat (0g
saturated fat); 31.8g carbohydrate;
623kJ (149 cal); 3.5g protein;
7.8g fibre*

grapefruit and blood orange juice

*preparation time 5 minutes
serves 1*

**2 small blood oranges (360g)
1 small grapefruit (350g)**

1 Juice oranges and grapefruit on
citrus squeezer; pour into glass.

*per serving 0.7g total fat (0g
saturated fat); 31.2g carbohydrate;
652kJ (156 cal); 4.6g protein;
6.5g fibre*

pear and ginger juice

preparation time 5 minutes
serves 1

2 medium pears (460g),
cut into wedges
2cm piece fresh ginger (10g)

1 Push ingredients through juice extractor into glass; stir to combine.

per serving 0.5g total fat
(0g saturated fat); 52.6g
carbohydrate; 882kJ (211 cal);
1.3g protein; 9.8g fibre

orange, mango and strawberry juice

preparation time 5 minutes
serves 1

2 small oranges (360g)
1 small mango (300g), chopped
coarsely
3 strawberries (60g), chopped
coarsely

1 Juice oranges on citrus squeezer; pour into glass.
2 Blend mango and strawberries until smooth; stir into orange juice.

per serving 0.7g total fat (0g
saturated fat); 48.7g carbohydrate;
949kJ (227 cal); 5.7g protein;
9.6g fibre

orange, carrot and celery juice

preparation time 5 minutes
serves 1

1 large orange (300g), peeled,
quartered
1 large carrot (180g), chopped
coarsely
1 trimmed celery stalk (100g),
chopped coarsely

1 Push orange, carrot and celery through juice extractor into glass; stir to combine.

per serving 0.5g total fat (0g
saturated fat); 28.6g carbohydrate;
573kJ (137 cal); 4.2g protein;
11.3g fibre

banana soy smoothie

preparation time 5 minutes
serves 1

1 cup (250ml) soy milk
1 small banana (130g),
chopped coarsely

1   Blend or process ingredients
until smooth; pour into glass.

per serving 2.1g total fat (0.2g
saturated fat); 8.2g carbohydrate;
255kJ (61 cal); 8.2g protein;
0.9g fibre

carrot, ginger and swiss chard juice

preparation time 5 minutes
serves 1

2 medium carrots (240g),
chopped coarsely
3 trimmed swiss chard leaves
(240g), chopped coarsely
2cm piece fresh ginger (10g)

1   Push ingredients through juice
extractor into glass; stir to combine.

per serving 0.7g total fat (0g
saturated fat); 14.5g carbohydrate;
364kJ (87 cal); 5.4g protein;
13.1g fibre

orange, carrot and ginger juice

preparation time 5 minutes
serves 1

2 medium oranges (480g),
peeled, quartered
1 small carrot (70g), chopped
coarsely
2cm piece fresh ginger (10g)

1   Push orange, carrot and ginger
through juice extractor into glass;
stir to combine.

per serving 0.4g total fat (0g
saturated fat); 30.6g carbohydrate;
606kJ (145 cal); 4g protein;
8.8g fibre

hot grapefruit water

preparation time 5 minutes
makes 1 litre

3½ cups (875ml) boiling water
½ cup (125ml) fresh grapefruit juice

1 Place the water in large jug; stir in juice.

per 250ml 0g total fat (0g saturated fat);
1.5g carbohydrate; 33kJ (8 cal); 0.3g protein;
0.4g fibre

hot lemon water

preparation time 5 minutes
makes 1 litre

3½ cups (875ml) boiling water
½ cup (125ml) fresh lemon juice

1 Place the water in large jug; stir in juice.
Serve with lemon slices, if desired.

per 250ml 0.1g total fat (0g saturated fat);
0.9g carbohydrate; 38kJ (9 cal); 0.2g protein;
0g fibre

lemongrass and kaffir lime tea

preparation time 5 minutes
cooking time 10 minutes
makes 1 litre

10cm stick (20g) finely chopped fresh lemongrass
4 fresh kaffir lime leaves
1 litre (4 cups) water

1 Combine ingredients in small saucepan; bring to a boil.
2 Reduce heat; simmer, uncovered, 5 minutes. Cool 5 minutes; strain.

per 250ml 0g total fat (0g saturated fat); 0g carbohydrate; 1kJ (0.3 cal); 0g protein; 0g fibre

cardamom and chamomile tea

preparation time 5 minutes
cooking time 10 minutes
makes 1 litre

2 tablespoons loose-leaf chamomile tea
4 cardamom pods, bruised
1 litre (4 cups) water

1 Combine ingredients in small saucepan; bring to a boil.
2 Reduce heat; simmer, uncovered, 5 minutes. Cool 5 minutes; strain.

per 250ml 0g total fat (0g saturated fat); 0g carbohydrate; 0.6kJ (0.2 cal); 0g protein; 0g fibre

almond milk

preparation time 5 minutes
(plus refrigeration time)
makes ¾ cup

1 cup (250ml) water
½ cup (70g) toasted slivered almonds
3 drops vanilla extract

1 Blend or process the water and nuts until pureed.
2 Strain mixture through muslin-lined sieve into small jug; discard solids. Add extract; stir to combine. Refrigerate until chilled.

per 180ml 38.1g total fat (3.8g saturated fat); 3.1g carbohydrate; 1697kJ (406 cal); 14.3g protein; 6.3g fibre

cinnamon and orange tea

preparation time 5 minutes
cooking time 10 minutes
makes 1 litre

2 cinnamon sticks
10cm strip orange rind
1 litre (4 cups) water

1 Combine ingredients in small saucepan; bring to a boil.
2 Reduce heat; simmer, uncovered, 5 minutes. Cool 5 minutes; strain.

per 250ml 0g total fat (0g saturated fat); 0.6g carbohydrate; 13kJ (3 cal); 0.1g protein; 0.2g fibre

mint tea

preparation time 5 minutes
makes 1 litre

½ cup coarsely chopped fresh mint leaves
1 litre (4 cups) boiling water

1 Combine ingredients in large heatproof jug.
2 Stand, uncovered, 3 minutes; strain.
TIP Any unused tea can be reheated in a microwave oven or served chilled.

per 250ml 0.1g total fat (0 saturated fat); 0.3g carbohydrate; 13kJ (3 cal); 0.2g protein; 0.5g fibre

ginger tea

preparation time 5 minutes
cooking time 20 minutes
makes 1 litre

20cm piece fresh ginger (100g), sliced thinly
1.5 litres (6 cups) water

1 Combine ingredients in medium saucepan; bring to a boil.
2 Reduce heat; simmer, uncovered, about 15 minutes or until liquid has reduced by a third. Cool 5 minutes; strain.
TIP Any unused tea can be reheated in a microwave oven or served chilled.

per 250ml 0.1g total fat (0 saturated fat); 1g carbohydrate; 29kJ (7 cal); 0.2g protein; 0.7g fibre

breakfast

apple and pear compote with dates

preparation time 5 minutes
cooking time 10 minutes
serves 1

1 small apple (130g)
1 small pear (180g)
2 tablespoons fresh lemon juice
⅓ cup (55g) pitted coarsely chopped dried dates
1 teaspoon finely grated orange rind
2 tablespoons fresh orange juice

1 Peel and core apple and pear; dice into 2cm pieces. Combine apple and pear in small saucepan with lemon juice; cook, covered, over low heat, about 10 minutes or until fruit softens.
2 Meanwhile, combine dates, rind and orange juice in small saucepan; cook, uncovered, over low heat, stirring occasionally, about 5 minutes or until liquid is absorbed.
3 Serve compote, warm or cold, topped with date mixture and finely shredded orange rind, if desired.

per serving 0.5g total fat; (0g saturated fat); 72.1g carbohydrate; 1242kJ (297 cal); 2.4g protein; 9.9g fibre

porridge with poached pears and blueberries*

preparation time 10 minutes
cooking time 10 minutes
serves 1

¾ cup (180ml) hot water
⅓ cup (30g) rolled oats
1 small pear (180g), cored, chopped coarsely
½ cup (125ml) cold water
2 tablespoons frozen blueberries, thawed

1 Combine the hot water and oats in small saucepan over medium heat; cook, stirring, about 5 minutes or until porridge is thick and creamy.
2 Meanwhile, place pear and the cold water in small saucepan; bring to a boil. Reduce heat; simmer, uncovered, about 5 minutes or until pear has softened. Serve porridge topped with pears and 1 tablespoon of the poaching liquid; sprinkle with berries.

per serving 2.7g total fat (0.5g saturated fat); 43.4g carbohydrate; 882kJ (211 cal); 3.9g protein; 6.6g fibre

before and after detox recipe

apple and blueberry muesli*

preparation time 10 minutes (plus refrigeration time)
serves 1

2 tablespoons rolled oats
⅓ cup (80ml) fresh apple juice
½ medium apple (75g), grated coarsely
⅓ cup (50g) blueberries
⅓ cup (95g) sheep's milk yogurt
1 tablespoon fresh apple juice, extra
1 tablespoon blueberries, extra

1 Combine oats and juice in small bowl, cover; refrigerate about 1 hour or until oats soften. Stir in apple, blueberries and yogurt.
2 Serve muesli drizzled with extra juice and topped with extra blueberries.

per serving 7.2g total fat (0.2g saturated fat); 39.7g carbohydrate; 1083kJ (259 cal); 6.7g protein; 3.9g fibre

before and after detox recipe

macerated fruits

preparation time 5 minutes (plus refrigeration time)
serves 1

¼ cup (20g) dried apples
¼ cup (35g) dried apricots
½ cup (125ml) fresh apple juice
2 teaspoons fresh lemon juice

1 Combine ingredients in small bowl.
2 Cover; refrigerate 2 hours or overnight.

per serving 0.2g total fat (0g saturated fat);
41.4g carbohydrate; 723kJ (173 cal); 1.9g protein;
5g fibre

four-fruit combo

preparation time 10 minutes
serves 1

1 small pear (180g), chopped coarsely
1 small apple (130g), chopped coarsely
1 small pink grapefruit (350g), segmented
100g red grapes

1 Combine ingredients in medium bowl.

per serving 0.8g total fat (0g saturated fat);
58.5g carbohydrate; 1066kJ (255 cal); 4.1g protein;
8.1g fibre

papaya with passionfruit and lime

preparation time 10 minutes
serves 1

1 small papaya (650g), cut into thick wedges
1 tablespoon fresh passionfruit pulp
2 teaspoons fresh lime juice

1 Place papaya on medium serving plate. Drizzle with passionfruit and juice.
TIP We used the red-fleshed Hawaiian or Fijian variety instead of the yellow-fleshed papaya here. You need one passionfruit for this recipe.

per serving 0.5g total fat (0g saturated fat); 32.3g carbohydrate; 598kJ (143 cal); 2.5g protein; 13.1g fibre

banana with passionfruit yogurt

preparation time 5 minutes
serves 1

2 tablespoons sheep's milk yogurt
2 tablespoons fresh passionfruit pulp
1 medium banana (200g), sliced thickly

1 Combine yogurt and half of the passionfruit in small bowl.
2 Place banana in small bowl; top with yogurt mixture and remaining passionfruit.
TIP You need two passionfruits for this recipe.

per serving 3.1g total fat (0g saturated fat); 31.2g carbohydrate; 757kJ (181 cal); 5.6g protein; 8.5g fibre

figs with sheep's milk yogurt and honey

preparation time 5 minutes
serves 1

2 medium fresh figs (120g), chopped coarsely
¼ cup (70g) sheep's milk yogurt
4 medium fresh figs (240g), halved
1 teaspoon honey

1 Combine chopped figs and yogurt in small bowl.
2 Place halved figs on serving plate; drizzle with honey.
3 Serve with yogurt mixture.

per serving 5.2g total fat (0g saturated fat);
35.2g carbohydrate; 932kJ (223 cal); 7.5g protein;
6.8g fibre

lychees with passionfruit

preparation time 5 minutes
serves 1

20 fresh lychees (500g)
2 tablespoons fresh passionfruit pulp

1 Blend or process half of the lychees until smooth;
stir in half of the passionfruit.
2 Place remaining lychees in small bowl; top with
lychee mixture and remaining passionfruit.
TIP You need one passionfruit for this recipe.

per serving 0.4g total fat (0g saturated fat);
62g carbohydrate; 1112kJ (266 cal); 4.8g protein;
7.8g fibre

kiwi fruit, lychee and lime salad

preparation time 5 minutes
serves 1

2 kiwi fruits (170g), cut into wedges
4 fresh lychees (100g)
1 tablespoon fresh mint leaves
1 tablespoon fresh lime juice

1 Combine ingredients in small bowl.

per serving 0.5g total fat (0g saturated fat);
26.8g carbohydrate; 535kJ (128 cal); 3.2g protein;
6.1g fibre

banana with passionfruit

preparation time 5 minutes
serves 1

2 medium bananas (400g)
1 tablespoon fresh passionfruit pulp

1 Cut bananas in half lengthways; cut each half into
two pieces.
2 Place banana in medium serving bowl; drizzle with
passionfruit pulp.
TIP You need one passionfruit for this recipe.

per serving 0.3g total fat (0g saturated fat);
54.5g carbohydrate; 999kJ (239 cal); 5.2g protein;
8.8g fibre

cherries and yogurt

preparation time 5 minutes
serves 1

1½ cups (225g) cherries
⅓ cup (95g) sheep's milk yogurt

1 Place cherries on small serving plate; serve with yogurt.

per serving 6g total fat (0g saturated fat); 23.4g carbohydrate; 757kJ (181 cal); 6g protein; 2.7g fibre

mango cheeks with lime wedges

preparation time 5 minutes
serves 1

1 large mango (600g)
½ lime, cut into wedges

1 Slice cheeks from mango; score each cheek in shallow criss-cross pattern, taking care not to cut through skin.
2 Serve mango cheeks with lime wedges.

per serving 1g total fat (0g saturated fat); 54.6g carbohydrate; 1074kJ (257 cal); 4.9g protein; 8g fibre

stewed prunes with orange

preparation time 5 minutes
cooking time 15 minutes
serves 1

½ cup (85g) pitted dried prunes
¼ cup (60ml) fresh orange juice
¼ cup (60ml) water
5cm strip orange rind, sliced thinly
1 cinnamon stick
2 cardamon pods, bruised

1 Place ingredients in small saucepan; bring to a boil. Reduce heat; simmer, covered, 10 minutes.
2 Serve stewed prunes with sheep's milk yogurt, if desired.

per serving 0.4g total fat (0g saturated fat); 42.2g carbohydrate; 752kJ (180 cal); 2.3g protein; 6.8g fibre

blood plums with honey and cardamom yogurt

preparation time 5 minutes serves 1

¼ cup (70g) sheep's milk yogurt
2 teaspoons honey
¼ teaspoon ground cardamom
2 small blood plums (180g), quartered

1 Combine yogurt, honey and cardamom in small bowl.
2 Place plums on small serving plate; drizzle with yogurt mixture.
TIP If you cannot get hold of blood plums, use very ripe purple plums.

per serving 4.4g total fat (0g saturated fat); 26.7g carbohydrate; 732kJ (175 cal); 4.2g protein; 3.6g fibre

soups

vegetable stock

preparation time 30 minutes
cooking time 1 hour 40 minutes
makes 2 litres

2 medium brown onions (300g), chopped coarsely
3 medium carrots (360g), chopped coarsely
3 medium parsnips (750g), chopped coarsely
2 medium swedes (450g), chopped coarsely
1 small fennel bulb (200g), chopped coarsely
1 large red pepper (350g), chopped coarsely
1 trimmed celery stalk (100g), chopped coarsely
2 cloves garlic, chopped coarsely
2 bay leaves
6 black peppercorns
4 litres (16 cups) water
1¼ cups coarsely chopped fresh flat-leaf parsley

1 Combine vegetables, bay leaves, peppercorns and the water in large stock pot or saucepan; bring to a boil. Reduce heat; simmer, uncovered, stirring occasionally, 1 hour. Add parsley; simmer, uncovered, 30 minutes.
2 Strain stock through muslin-lined sieve or colander; discard solids.
TIP Stock can be kept, covered, for up to a week in the refrigerator. Stock also suitable to freeze for up to three months.

per 250ml 0.4g total fat (0g saturated fat); 15.8g carbohydrate; 343kJ (82 cal); 3.8g protein; 6.5g fibre

roasted tomato and pepper soup

preparation time 10 minutes
cooking time 35 minutes
serves 1

4 large tomatoes (880g), chopped coarsely
1 large red pepper (350g), chopped coarsely
1 small brown onion (80g), chopped coarsely
2 cloves garlic, sliced thinly
1 tablespoon finely shredded fresh basil

1 Preheat oven to moderate (180°C/160°C fan-assisted).
2 Combine tomato, pepper, onion and garlic in small baking dish; roast, covered, about 30 minutes or until vegetables soften.
3 Push vegetables through mouli or fine sieve into small saucepan; discard solids.
4 Reheat soup; serve soup topped with basil.

per serving 1.6g total fat (0g saturated fat); 33.1g carbohydrate; 895kJ (214 cal); 14.9g protein; 15.4g fibre

pumpkin and sweet potato soup

preparation time 15 minutes
cooking time 25 minutes
serves 1

1 teaspoon olive oil
1 small brown onion (80g), chopped coarsely
1 clove garlic, crushed
200g pumpkin, chopped coarsely
1 small sweet potato (250g), chopped coarsely
2 cups (500ml) vegetable stock (page 50)
¼ teaspoon finely grated orange rind
1 tablespoon fresh orange juice
1 tablespoon finely chopped fresh chives

1 Heat oil in medium saucepan; cook onion and garlic, stirring, until onion softens.
2 Add pumpkin, sweet potato and stock; bring to a boil. Reduce heat; simmer, covered, about 15 minutes or until pumpkin and sweet potato are tender. Cool 10 minutes.
3 Blend or process pumpkin mixture until smooth.
4 Return soup mixture to same pan with rind and juice; stir over heat, without boiling, until heated through.
5 Serve soup topped with chives.

per serving 6g total fat (1.3g saturated fat); 60.1g carbohydrate; 1438kJ (344 cal); 12.2g protein; 12.2g fibre

vegetable soup

preparation time 10 minutes
cooking time 20 minutes
serves 1

2 cups (500ml) vegetable stock (page 50)
1 trimmed corn cob (250g)
½ cup (50g) coarsely chopped cauliflower
½ small carrot (35g), diced into 1cm pieces
30g mangetout, trimmed, sliced thinly
1 spring onion, sliced thinly

1 Bring stock to a boil in small saucepan. Cut kernels from corn cob, add to pan with cauliflower and carrot; return to a boil. Reduce heat; simmer, covered, about 10 minutes or until cauliflower is just tender.
2 Stir in mangetout and onion; simmer, uncovered, 2 minutes.

per serving 2.7g total fat (0.2g saturated fat); 45g carbohydrate; 1074kJ (257 cal); 12.6g protein; 15.3g fibre

leek and potato soup

preparation time 10 minutes
cooking time 25 minutes
serves 1

1 teaspoon olive oil
1 clove garlic, crushed
½ teaspoon fresh thyme leaves
1 small leek (200g), sliced thinly
1 medium potato (200g), chopped coarsely
2 cups (500ml) vegetable stock (page 50)
½ spring onion, sliced thinly

1 Heat oil in small saucepan; cook garlic, thyme and leek, stirring, about 3 minutes or until leek softens. Add potato and stock; bring to a boil. Reduce heat; simmer, covered, about 15 minutes or until potato is tender.
2 Blend or process leek mixture until smooth.
3 Reheat soup; serve soup topped with onion.

per serving 5.5g total fat (0.7g saturated fat); 38.5g carbohydrate; 1016kJ (243 cal); 9.3g protein; 11.1g fibre

lentil and vegetable soup

preparation time 10 minutes
cooking time 45 minutes
serves 1

2 cups (500ml) vegetable stock (page 50)
¼ cup (50g) french green lentils
1 clove garlic, crushed
½ untrimmed celery stalk (75g)
1 medium carrot (120g), chopped coarsely
50g mushrooms, chopped coarsely
2 tablespoons coarsely chopped fresh
flat-leaf parsley

1 Combine stock, lentils, garlic and celery leaves in small saucepan; bring to a boil. Reduce heat; simmer, covered, about 20 minutes or until lentils just soften. Discard celery leaves.
2 Add coarsely chopped celery stalk, carrot and mushroom; bring to a boil. Reduce heat; simmer, covered, about 15 minutes or until vegetables are tender. Stir in parsley.
TIPS French green lentils have a sensational nutty, earthy flavour and stand up well to being boiled without becoming muddy. They are available at specialist food shops and better delicatessens. You need the leaves from the celery stalk for this recipe.

per serving 1.7g total fat (0.2g saturated fat); 37.5g carbohydrate; 978kJ (234 cal); 18g protein; 17.7g fibre

asian broth

preparation time 15 minutes (plus standing time)
cooking time 10 minutes
serves 1

5 dried shiitake mushrooms (10g)
1½ cups (375ml) vegetable stock (page 50)
2 teaspoons tamari
1cm piece fresh ginger (5g), grated
½ teaspoon groundnut oil
½ small carrot (35g), sliced thinly
30g mangetout, trimmed, chopped coarsely
1 spring onion, sliced thinly
½ cup (40g) finely shredded chinese cabbage
30g canned bamboo shoots, cut into matchsticks

1 Place mushrooms in small heatproof bowl, cover with boiling water, stand 20 minutes; drain. Discard stems; halve caps.
2 Combine stock, tamari, ginger and oil in medium saucepan; bring to a boil. Add mushroom and carrot, reduce heat; simmer, covered, until carrot is just tender. Add mangetout, onion, cabbage and bamboo shoots; simmer, uncovered, 2 minutes.

per serving 2.6g total fat (0.4g saturated fat); 13.8g carbohydrate; 410kJ (98 cal); 4.6g protein; 6.6g fibre

vegetable and soba soup

preparation time 15 minutes
cooking time 15 minutes
serves 1

2 cups (500ml) vegetable stock (page 50)
1 teaspoon tamari
5cm piece fresh ginger (25g), grated
2 cloves garlic, crushed
1 small carrot (70g), cut into matchsticks
50g mangetout, trimmed, sliced thinly lengthways
50g soba noodles

1 Combine stock, tamari, ginger and garlic in small saucepan; bring to a boil. Reduce heat; simmer, covered, 5 minutes. Add carrot and mangetout; simmer, uncovered, about 3 minutes or until carrot is tender.
2 Meanwhile, cook noodles in small saucepan of boiling water, uncovered, until just tender; drain.
3 Place noodles in serving bowl; ladle soup over noodles.
TIP Soba is a Japanese noodle, similar in appearance to spaghetti, made from buckwheat.

per serving 1.2g total fat (0.2g saturated fat); 51.8g carbohydrate; 1108kJ (265 cal); 10.9g protein; 10.5g fibre

light meals and salads

lamb's lettuce salad with pecans and orange

preparation time 10 minutes
serves 1

20g watercress
25g lamb's lettuce
30g mangetout sprouts, trimmed
⅓ cup (45g) toasted pecans, chopped coarsely
2 teaspoons olive oil
2 small oranges (360g)

1 Place watercress, lettuce, sprouts, nuts and oil in medium bowl.
2 Segment oranges over salad to save juice. Add orange segments to bowl; toss gently to combine.
TIP Lamb's lettuce, also known as mâche or corn salad, has a mild, almost nutty, flavour and tender, narrow, dark green leaves. You need a 225g punnet for this recipe. It is available from most greengrocers.

per serving 42.1g total fat (3.4g saturated fat); 29.8g carbohydrate; 2241kJ (536 cal); 10.6g protein; 11.6g fibre

vegetable wrap*

preparation time 15 minutes
serves 1

1 slice lavash bread
¼ small avocado (50g)
1 teaspoon tahini
½ cup (60g) coarsely grated uncooked beetroot
⅓ cup (50g) coarsely grated uncooked pumpkin
¼ small red pepper (40g), sliced thinly
40g mushrooms, sliced thinly
¼ small red onion (25g), sliced thinly

1 Spread bread with avocado and tahini.
2 Place remaining ingredients on long side of bread; roll to enclose filling.
TIP Lavash is a flat, unleavened bread, originally from the Mediterranean. If you cannot find lavash, use wholemeal tortilla wraps instead.

per serving 13.4g total fat (2.6g saturated fat); 45.1g carbohydrate; 1463kJ (350 cal); 12.2g protein; 10.1g fibre

before and after detox recipe

goat's cheese, salad and pecan sandwich*

preparation time 15 minutes
serves 1

40g goat's milk cheese
1 tablespoon finely chopped pecans
1 tablespoon coarsely chopped fresh flat-leaf parsley
2 slices wholemeal bread (90g)
1 small tomato (90g), sliced thinly
¼ cucumber (65g), sliced thinly lengthways
½ small carrot (35g), sliced thinly lengthways
2 small baby cos lettuce leaves

1 Combine cheese, nuts and parsley in small bowl.
2 Spread cheese mixture on each slice of bread; top one slice with tomato, cucumber, carrot and lettuce. Top with remaining slice.

per serving 16.5g total fat (5g saturated fat); 40.8g carbohydrate; 1593kJ (381 cal); 17.1g protein; 10.6g fibre

before and after detox recipe

open rye sandwich*

preparation time 10 minutes
serves 1

1 teaspoon finely chopped fresh basil
1 teaspoon finely chopped fresh mint
1 teaspoon finely chopped fresh flat-leaf parsley
1 tablespoon ricotta cheese
1 slice rye bread (40g)
½ cup (10g) loosely packed baby rocket leaves
1 small tomato (90g), sliced thinly
¼ cucumber (65g), sliced thinly
1 tablespoon alfalfa sprouts

1 Combine herbs and cheese in small bowl.
2 Spread cheese mixture on bread; top with remaining ingredients.

per serving 3.7g total fat (1.7g saturated fat); 21.8g carbohydrate; 635kJ (152 cal); 7.6g protein; 4.9g fibre

before and after detox recipe

vegetable stir-fry*

preparation time 10 minutes
cooking time 10 minutes
serves 1

1 teaspoon sesame oil
100g fresh shiitake mushrooms, sliced thickly
1 medium carrot (120g), sliced thinly
2 tablespoons water
100g broccoli, sliced thinly
75g mangetout, trimmed, sliced thickly
1 tablespoon tamari
1 spring onion, sliced thinly

1 Heat oil in wok; stir-fry mushroom and carrot for 2 minutes. Add the water; stir-fry 5 minutes or until carrot just softens. Add broccoli and mangetout; stir-fry until broccoli is just tender. Stir in tamari.
2 Serve stir-fry topped with onion.

per serving 5.4g total fat (0.8g saturated fat); 23.7g carbohydrate; 778kJ (186 cal); 10.8g protein; 11.7g fibre

before and after detox recipe

beetroot dip

preparation time 5 minutes
serves 1

225g can beetroot slices, drained
¼ cup (70g) sheep's milk yogurt

1 Blend or process beetroot with yogurt.
2 Serve beetroot dip sprinkled with coarsely chopped chives, if desired.

per serving 4.4g total fat (0g saturated fat); 17.6g carbohydrate; 569kJ (136 cal); 5.3g protein; 4g fibre

raita

preparation time 10 minutes
serves 1

½ cup (140g) sheep's milk yogurt
¼ cucumber (65g), chopped finely
1 tablespoon finely chopped fresh coriander
1 clove garlic, crushed
2 teaspoons fresh lemon juice

1 Combine ingredients in small bowl.

per serving 3.8g total fat (0g saturated fat); 3.9g carbohydrate; 293kJ (70 cal); 3.2g protein; 0.7g fibre

These yummy dips are best served with assorted crudités such as carrot, cucumber and pepper sticks.

carrot dip

preparation time 10 minutes
cooking time 10 minutes
serves 1

1 medium carrot (120g), grated coarsely
½ cup (125ml) fresh orange juice
2 tablespoons goat's milk yogurt
1 tablespoon finely chopped fresh mint
1 tablespoon currants
1cm piece fresh ginger (5g), grated

1 Place carrot and juice in small saucepan; cook, uncovered, over low heat, about 10 minutes or until liquid is evaporated. Cool 10 minutes.
2 Blend or process carrot mixture with yogurt; stir in mint, currants and ginger.

per serving 2.2g total fat (1.2g saturated fat); 26g carbohydrate; 569kJ (136 cal); 3.8g protein; 4.4g fibre

hummus

preparation time 5 minutes
cooking time 15 minutes
serves 1

1½ cups (375ml) water
300g can chickpeas, drained, rinsed
2 tablespoons fresh lemon juice
1 clove garlic, quartered

1 Place the water and chickpeas in small saucepan; bring to a boil. Boil, uncovered, 10 minutes. Strain chickpeas over small bowl; reserve ⅓ cup cooking liquid. Cool 10 minutes.
2 Blend or process chickpeas, juice and garlic with reserved cooking liquid until just smooth.
3 Serve hummus sprinkled with finely chopped fresh flat-leaf parsley, if desired.

per serving 4.3g total fat (0.6g saturated fat); 28.5g carbohydrate; 861kJ (206 cal); 13g protein; 9.9g fibre

white bean salad*

preparation time 15 minutes
serves 1

50g mixed salad leaves
½ cup (100g) canned white beans, rinsed, drained
2 tablespoons coarsely chopped fresh tarragon
2 tablespoons coarsely chopped fresh flat-leaf parsley
1 small carrot (70g), cut into matchsticks
¼ cucumber (65g), cut into matchsticks
2 red radishes (70g), trimmed, cut into matchsticks
2 tablespoons fresh apple juice
1 tablespoon apple cider vinegar
1 tablespoon toasted sunflower seeds
1 tablespoon toasted pepitas

1 Place salad leaves, beans, herbs, carrot, cucumber, radish, juice and vinegar in medium bowl; toss gently to combine.
2 Serve salad topped with seeds.
TIP Many varieties of pre-cooked white beans are available canned, among them cannellini, butter and haricot beans; any of these are suitable for this salad.

per serving 12.3g total fat (0.5g saturated fat); 21g carbohydrate; 1145kJ (274 cal); 10.1g protein; 12.5g fibre

before and after detox recipe

mixed bean salad*

preparation time 15 minutes
serves 1

1 clove garlic, crushed
2 teaspoons olive oil
2 teaspoons fresh lemon juice
½ x 300g can four-bean mix, rinsed, drained
1 trimmed celery stalk (100g), chopped finely
½ medium yellow pepper (100g), chopped finely
¼ cup (30g) pitted black olives, chopped coarsely
¼ cup loosely packed fresh flat-leaf parsley leaves
½ small red onion (50g), sliced thinly
1 cup (20g) loosely packed baby rocket leaves

1 Place garlic, oil and juice in screw-top jar; shake well.
2 Place remaining ingredients and dressing in medium bowl; toss gently to combine.

per serving 10.3g total fat (1.5g saturated fat); 27.6g carbohydrate; 995kJ (238 cal); 9.3g protein; 10.5g fibre

before and after detox recipe

asparagus caesar salad*

preparation time 15 minutes
cooking time 10 minutes
serves 1

1 slice wholemeal bread (45g), crust removed
1 teaspoon olive oil
½ clove garlic, crushed
170g asparagus, trimmed, chopped coarsely
½ baby cos lettuce (90g), leaves separated

CAESAR DRESSING
½ clove garlic, crushed
1 teaspoon american mustard
2 teaspoons lemon juice
2 tablespoons sheep's milk yogurt
1 tablespoon water

1 Preheat oven to moderate (180°C/160°C fan-assisted).
2 Cut bread into 3cm cubes. Combine oil and garlic in small bowl, add bread; toss bread to coat in mixture. Place bread, in single layer, on oven tray; toast, uncovered, 10 minutes.
3 Meanwhile, place ingredients for caesar dressing in screw-top jar; shake well.
4 Boil, steam or microwave chpped asparagus until just tender; drain.
5 Place croutons and asparagus in medium bowl with lettuce; toss gently to combine.
6 Serve salad drizzled with dressing.

per serving 9g total fat (0.8g saturated fat); 19.7g carbohydrate; 865kJ (207 cal); 10.2g protein; 6.7g fibre

*before and after detox recipe

green vegetable salad with american mustard dressing

preparation time 10 minutes
cooking time 10 minutes
serves 1

50g green beans, trimmed
50g mangetout, trimmed
50g sugar snap peas, trimmed
¼ cup loosely packed fresh flat-leaf parsley leaves
2 tablespoons fresh chervil leaves
1 cup (25g) baby rocket leaves
1 tablespoon currants

AMERICAN MUSTARD DRESSING
2 teaspoons american mustard
2 teaspoons fresh lemon juice
2 teaspoons olive oil

1 Boil, steam or microwave beans and peas, separately, until just tender; drain. Rinse beans, mangetout and peas under cold water; drain.
2 Meanwhile, place ingredients for american mustard dressing in screw-top jar; shake well.
3 Place beans, mangetout and peas in medium bowl with herbs, rocket and currants; toss gently to combine.
4 Serve salad drizzled with dressing.

per serving 9.9g total fat (1.3g saturated fat); 15g carbohydrate; 715kJ (171 cal); 5.7g protein; 5.6g fibre

spinach and courgette salad with yogurt hummus

preparation time 25 minutes (plus standing time)
cooking time 30 minutes
serves 1

½ cup (100g) dried chickpeas
1 small courgette (90g), sliced thickly
1 clove garlic, unpeeled
2 tablespoons fresh lemon juice
2 teaspoons tahini
1 tablespoon goat's milk yogurt
60g baby spinach leaves
½ small red onion (50g), sliced thinly

1 Place chickpeas in small bowl, cover with water; stand overnight, drain. Rinse under cold water; drain.
2 Cook chickpeas in small saucepan of boiling water, uncovered, until just tender; drain over small bowl, reserve 2 teaspoons of the liquid. Rinse chickpeas under cold water; drain.
3 Meanwhile, cook courgette and garlic on heated lightly oiled grill plate (or grill or barbecue) until browned both sides. When cool enough to handle, peel garlic.
4 Blend or process ¼ cup cooked chickpeas, juice, tahini, yogurt, reserved liquid and garlic until smooth.
5 Place spinach, onion and remaining chickpeas in medium bowl; toss gently to combine.
6 Serve salad drizzled with yogurt hummus.

per serving 14.6g total fat (2.3g saturated fat); 43.4g carbohydrate; 1701kJ (407 cal); 24.3g protein; 18.8g fibre

greek salad

preparation time 10 minutes
serves 1

½ baby cos lettuce (90g), leaves separated
1 medium tomato (150g), cut into thick wedges
½ small red pepper (75g), chopped coarsely
½ cucumber (130g), chopped coarsely
¼ cup (40g) pitted kalamata olives
50g goat's milk feta, crumbled
2 teaspoons fresh lemon juice
2 teaspoons olive oil

1 Place ingredients in large bowl; toss gently to combine.

per serving 18.1g total fat (6.6g saturated fat); 19.5g carbohydrate; 1196kJ (286 cal); 11.3g protein; 6.5g fibre

tomato and avocado salad with tofu pesto

preparation time 10 minutes
serves 1

1 medium tomato (150g), cut into wedges
½ medium avocado (125g), sliced thickly
100g firm silken tofu, diced into 3cm pieces
50g mixed salad leaves
1 tablespoon fresh basil leaves

TOFU PESTO
1 tablespoon toasted pine nuts
50g firm tofu
½ cup firmly packed fresh basil leaves
1 tablespoon fresh lemon juice
1 tablespoon water

1 Blend or process tofu pesto ingredients until smooth.
2 Combine salad ingredients together; serve with pesto.

per serving 40.6g total fat (6.4g saturated fat); 7g carbohydrate; 2044kJ (489 cal); 24g protein; 8.6g fibre

pear, spinach, walnut and celery salad

preparation time 10 minutes
serves 1

1 large pear (330g), cut into thin wedges
60g baby spinach leaves
¼ cup (25g) toasted walnuts, chopped coarsely
1 trimmed celery stalk (100g), chopped coarsely

MUSTARD DRESSING

2 teaspoons american mustard
1 teaspoon cider vinegar
1 tablespoon fresh apple juice

1 Place ingredients for mustard dressing in screw-top jar; shake well.
2 Place pear, spinach, nuts and celery in medium bowl; toss gently to combine.
3 Serve salad drizzled with dressing.

per serving 18.1g total fat (1.1g saturated fat); 50.5g carbohydrate; 1601kJ (383 cal); 6.9g protein; 12.1g fibre

pearl barley salad

preparation time 10 minutes
cooking time 25 minutes
serves 1

½ cup (100g) pearl barley
125g asparagus, trimmed, cut into 4cm lengths
125g cherry tomatoes, halved
¼ cucumber (65g), sliced thinly
¾ cup (45g) finely shredded iceberg lettuce
2 tablespoons coarsely chopped fresh basil
2 tablespoons fresh lemon juice

1 Cook barley in small saucepan of boiling water, uncovered, about 25 minutes or until tender; drain. Cool 10 minutes.
2 Meanwhile, boil, steam or microwave asparagus until just tender; drain.
3 Place barley and asparagus in medium bowl with remaining ingredients; toss gently to combine.

per serving 2.9g total fat (0.4g saturated fat); 68.4g carbohydrate; 1513kJ (362 cal); 13.5g protein; 17g fibre

potato and bean salad with lemon yogurt dressing

preparation time 15 minutes
cooking time 15 minutes
serves 1

2 small potatoes (240g), unpeeled, cut into wedges
150g green beans, trimmed, cut into 3cm lengths
1 cup (230g) baby rocket leaves
½ small red onion (50g), sliced thinly

LEMON YOGURT DRESSING
⅓ cup (95g) sheep's milk yogurt
1 teaspoon finely grated lemon rind
1 tablespoon fresh lemon juice
1 tablespoon finely chopped fresh flat-leaf parsley

1 Boil, steam or microwave potato and beans, separately, until tender; drain. Rinse beans under cold water; drain.
2 Meanwhile, combine ingredients for lemon yogurt dressing in small bowl.
3 Place potato and beans in medium bowl with rocket and onion; toss gently to combine. Serve salad drizzled with dressing.

per serving 6.6g total fat (1g saturated fat); 43.9g carbohydrate; 1308kJ (313 cal); 15.2g protein; 10.3g fibre

cos, mangetout and roast celeriac salad

preparation time 15 minutes
cooking time 20 minutes
serves 1

100g celeriac, chopped coarsely
4 cloves garlic, unpeeled
cooking-oil spray
50g baby green beans, trimmed, chopped coarsely
2 tablespoons fresh lemon juice
2 teaspoons walnut oil
½ baby cos lettuce (90g), torn
50g mangetout, trimmed, sliced thinly
½ cup (50g) toasted walnuts, chopped coarsely

1 Preheat oven to very hot (240°C/220°C fan-assisted).
2 Place celeriac and garlic on shallow oven tray; spray with oil. Roast, uncovered, about 20 minutes or until celeriac is just tender and garlic softens.
3 Meanwhile, boil, steam or microwave beans until tender; drain. Rinse under cold water; drain.
4 When garlic is cool enough to handle, squeeze garlic flesh from skins into screw-top jar. Add juice and oil; shake well.
5 Place celeriac and beans in medium bowl with lettuce, mangetout, nuts and dressing; toss gently to combine.

per serving 46.9g total fat (13.2g saturated fat); 14g carbohydrate; 2215kJ (530 cal); 13.7g protein; 14.1g fibre

pan-fried tofu with vietnamese coleslaw salad

preparation time 20 minutes
cooking time 5 minutes
serves 1

100g firm silken tofu
1 small carrot (70g)
½ cup (40g) finely shredded green cabbage
½ cup (40g) finely shredded red cabbage
½ small yellow pepper (75g), sliced thinly
½ cup (40g) beansprouts
2 spring onions, sliced thinly
¼ cup loosely packed fresh coriander leaves

LIME AND GARLIC DRESSING
¼ cup (60ml) fresh lime juice
1 clove garlic, crushed

1 Place tofu, in single layer, on absorbent-paper-lined tray; cover tofu with more absorbent paper, stand 10 minutes.
2 Meanwhile, using vegetable peeler, slice carrot into ribbons. Place in medium bowl with cabbages, pepper, beansprouts, spring onion and coriander; toss gently to combine.
3 Place ingredients for lime and garlic dressing in screw-top jar; shake well.
4 Cut tofu into four slices; cook tofu in heated lightly oiled small frying pan until browned both sides.
5 Drizzle dressing over salad; serve with tofu.

per serving 7.4g total fat (1g saturated fat);
11.9g carbohydrate; 798kJ (191 cal); 17.5g protein;
10.3g fibre

potato and asparagus salad with yogurt and mint dressing

preparation time 20 minutes
cooking time 20 minutes
serves 1

150g baby new potatoes, unpeeled
125g asparagus, trimmed, cut into 3cm lengths
¼ cucumber (65g), sliced thinly
40g watercress, trimmed
¼ cup (40g) toasted pepitas

YOGURT AND MINT DRESSING
2 tablespoons sheep's milk yogurt
1 teaspoon finely grated lime rind
2 teaspoons fresh lime juice
¼ cup finely chopped fresh mint

1 Boil, steam or microwave potatoes until tender; drain. When cool enough to handle, quarter potatoes.
2 Meanwhile, boil, steam or microwave asparagus until tender; drain. Rinse under cold water; drain.
3 Combine ingredients for yogurt and mint dressing in small bowl.
4 Place potato and asparagus in medium bowl with cucumber, watercress, pepitas and dressing; toss gently to combine.

per serving 16.8g total fat (1g saturated fat); 25.7g carbohydrate; 1672kJ (400 cal); 10.7g protein; 11.8g fibre

chickpea, watercress and pepper salad

preparation time 15 minutes (plus standing time)
cooking time 30 minutes
serves 1

¼ cup (50g) dried chickpeas
100g watercress
1 tablespoon water
1 clove garlic, quartered
¼ cup (35g) toasted slivered almonds
¼ cup (60ml) fresh lemon juice
⅓ small red pepper (50g), sliced thinly
⅓ small yellow pepper (50g), sliced thinly

1 Place chickpeas in small bowl, cover with water; stand overnight, drain. Rinse under cold water; drain.
2 Cook chickpeas in small saucepan of boiling water, uncovered, until just tender; drain. Rinse under cold water; drain.
3 Trim watercress; reserve stalks. Blend or process watercress stalks with the water, garlic, a third of the chickpeas, 1 tablespoon of the nuts and 2 tablespoons of the juice until smooth. Transfer to medium bowl; stir in remaining chickpeas and remaining nuts.
4 Place watercress leaves and peppers in medium bowl with remaining juice; toss gently to combine. Top with chickpea mixture.

per serving 21.4g total fat (1.5g saturated fat); 15.8g carbohydrate; 1371kJ (328 cal); 16g protein; 11.4g fibre

borlotti bean, brown rice and almond salad

preparation time 10 minutes (plus standing time)
cooking time 20 minutes
serves 1

¼ cup (50g) dried borlotti beans
¼ cup (50g) brown long-grain rice
½ small red onion (50g), chopped finely
¼ cup finely chopped fresh flat-leaf parsley
¼ cup finely chopped fresh mint
1 medium tomato (150g), chopped finely
1 tablespoon toasted slivered almonds
2 tablespoons fresh lemon juice
2 teaspoons olive oil

1 Place beans in small bowl, cover with water; stand overnight, drain. Rinse under cold water; drain.
2 Cook beans in small saucepan of boiling water, uncovered, until just tender; drain. Rinse under cold water; drain.
3 Meanwhile, cook rice in small saucepan of boiling water, uncovered, until rice is tender; drain. Rinse under cold water; drain.
4 Place beans and rice in medium bowl with remaining ingredients; toss gently to combine.

per serving 18.4g total fat (2.1g saturated fat); 63.4g carbohydrate; 2140kJ (512 cal); 21.3g protein; 13.4g fibre

roasted plum tomatoes with barley salad

preparation time 15 minutes
cooking time 20 minutes
serves 1

¼ cup (50g) pearl barley
2 medium plum tomatoes (150g), cut into thick wedges
1 small green pepper (150g), chopped finely
½ small red onion (50g), chopped finely
½ cup coarsely chopped fresh flat-leaf parsley
LEMON AND DILL DRESSING
2 tablespoons fresh lemon juice
1 tablespoon finely chopped fresh dill
1 teaspoon olive oil
1 clove garlic, crushed

1 Preheat oven to very hot (240°C/220°C fan-assisted).
2 Cook barley in small saucepan of boiling water, uncovered, about 20 minutes or until just tender; drain. Rinse under cold water; drain.
3 Meanwhile, place tomato, cut-side up, on lightly oiled oven tray. Roast tomato, uncovered, about 15 minutes or until just softened.
4 Place ingredients for lemon and dill dressing in screw-top jar; shake well.
5 Place barley and half of the tomato in medium bowl with pepper, onion, parsley and dressing; toss gently to combine. Top with remaining tomato.

per serving 6.4g total fat (0.9g saturated fat); 44.4g carbohydrate; 1191kJ (285 cal); 10.7g protein; 13.4g fibre

soba salad with seaweed, ginger and vegetables

preparation time 10 minutes
cooking time 5 minutes
serves 1

5g wakame
50g soba
½ cucumber (130g), seeded, cut into matchsticks
1 small carrot (70g), cut into matchsticks
1 tablespoon toasted sesame seeds
1 spring onion, sliced thinly
1cm piece fresh ginger (5g), grated
1 teaspoon sesame oil
2 tablespoons fresh lime juice
1 teaspoon tamari

1 Place wakame in small bowl, cover with cold water; stand about 10 minutes or until wakame softens, drain. Discard any hard stems; chop coarsely.
2 Meanwhile, cook soba in small saucepan of boiling water, uncovered, until just tender; drain. Rinse under cold water; drain. Chop soba coarsely.
3 ingredients; toss gently to combine.
TIPS Wakame, a bright green seaweed usually sold in dried form, is used in soups, salads and seasonings. Dried wakame must be softened by soaking for about 10 minutes, and any hard stems are then discarded. It is available from most Asian food stores.
Soba is a Japanese noodle, similar in appearance to spaghetti, made from buckwheat.

per serving 12.2g total fat (1.6g saturated fat); 41.5g carbohydrate; 1367kJ (327 cal); 11.1g protein; 9.1g fibre

grilled asparagus with warm tomato dressing

preparation time 20 minutes
cooking time 15 minutes
serves 1

1 medium tomato (150g), chopped finely
1 clove garlic, crushed
2 tablespoons fresh lemon juice
1 tablespoon finely chopped fresh basil
1 tablespoon finely chopped fresh flat-leaf parsley
125g asparagus, trimmed
25g curly endive, torn
25g rocket leaves

1 Combine tomato, garlic and juice in small saucepan; bring to a boil. Reduce heat; simmer, uncovered, 2 minutes. Remove from heat; stir in herbs.
2 Meanwhile, cook asparagus on heated lightly oiled grill plate (or grill or barbecue) until just tender.
3 Place endive and rocket on medium serving plate; top with asparagus and tomato mixture.

per serving 0.7g total fat (0g saturated fat); 6.7g carbohydrate; 272kJ (65 cal); 6.3g protein; 6.5g fibre

thai soya bean salad with grapes and pink grapefruit

preparation time 15 minutes (plus standing time)
cooking time 20 minutes
serves 1

¼ cup (50g) dried soya beans
1 small pink grapefruit (350g), segmented
50g green grapes, halved
1 small white onion (80g), chopped finely
50g mangetout sprouts, trimmed
¼ cup finely chopped fresh coriander
¼ cup finely chopped fresh mint
1 fresh kaffir lime leaf, shredded finely
2 tablespoons fresh lime juice

1 Place beans in small bowl, cover with water; stand overnight, drain. Rinse under cold water; drain.
2 Cook beans in small saucepan of boiling water, uncovered, until just tender; drain. Rinse under cold water; drain.
3 Place beans in medium bowl with remaining ingredients; toss gently to combine.

per serving 11.3g total fat (1.6g saturated fat); 38.3g carbohydrate; 1517kJ (363 cal); 24.6g protein; 16.9g fibre

baked beetroot salad with cannellini beans, feta and mint

preparation time 10 minutes (plus standing time)
cooking time 50 minutes
serves 1

¼ cup (50g) dried cannellini beans
1 medium beetroot (175g), diced into 3cm pieces
cooking-oil spray
50g goat's feta cheese, crumbled
50g mixed salad leaves
¼ cup loosely packed fresh mint leaves
APPLE DRESSING
2 tablespoons fresh apple juice
2 teaspoons american mustard

1 Place beans in small bowl, cover with water; stand overnight, drain. Rinse under cold water; drain.
2 Cook beans in small saucepan of boiling water, uncovered, until just tender; drain. Rinse under cold water; drain.
3 Preheat oven to moderately hot (200°C/180°C fan-assisted).
4 Place beetroot in small shallow baking dish; spray with oil. Bake, covered, about 20 minutes or until tender.
5 Place ingredients for apple dressing in screw-top jar; shake well.
6 Place beans and beetroot in medium bowl with remaining ingredients and dressing; toss gently to combine.

per serving 10.3g total fat (5.4g saturated fat); 39.4g carbohydrate; 1417kJ (339 cal); 21.7g protein; 16.3g fibre

roasted pumpkin, pecan and feta salad

preparation time 15 minutes
cooking time 20 minutes
serves 1

100g pumpkin, chopped coarsely
cooking-oil spray
80g rocket leaves
⅓ cup (40g) toasted pecans
50g goat's feta cheese, crumbled
CITRUS DRESSING
1 tablespoon fresh orange juice
1 tablespoon fresh lemon juice
1 teaspoon grapeseed oil

1 Preheat oven to very hot (240°C/220°C fan-assisted).
2 Place pumpkin on lightly oiled oven tray; spray with oil. Roast, uncovered, about 20 minutes or until tender.
3 Place ingredients for citrus dressing in screw-top jar; shake well.
4 Combine pumpkin in medium bowl with remaining ingredients and dressing; toss gently to combine.

per serving 44.3g total fat (7.9g saturated fat); 12.7g carbohydrate; 2111kJ (505 cal); 14.9g protein; 5.8g fibre

orange, fennel and almond salad

preparation time 10 minutes
cooking time 10 minutes
serves 1

⅓ cup (80ml) fresh orange juice
2 teaspoons almond oil
1 baby fennel bulb (130g)
1 large orange (300g), segmented
50g baby spinach leaves
¼ cup (20g) flaked almonds

1 Place juice in small saucepan; bring to a boil. Boil, uncovered, until juice reduces to 1 tablespoon; cool 10 minutes. Combine juice with oil in small jug.
2 Meanwhile, reserve fennel tips from fennel; slice fennel thinly.
3 Place fennel in medium bowl with orange, spinach and nuts; toss gently to combine.
4 Serve salad drizzled with dressing and sprinkled with fennel tips.

per serving 20.8g total fat (1.5g saturated fat); 26.5g carbohydrate; 1363kJ (326 cal); 8.5g protein; 9.6g fibre

main courses

stir-fried asian greens with tofu

preparation time 10 minutes
cooking time 10 minutes
serves 1

2 teaspoons groundnut oil
2cm piece fresh ginger (10g), cut into slivers
1 clove garlic, crushed
100g gai larn, chopped coarsely
100g tenderstem broccoli, chopped coarsely
150g baby pak choy, chopped coarsely
100g firm tofu, chopped coarsely
1 tablespoon water
2 teaspoons tamari
2 teaspoons coarsely chopped toasted peanuts

1 Heat oil in wok; stir-fry ginger and garlic until fragrant.
Add vegetables, tofu, the water and tamari; stir-fry until greens
are just tender.
2 Serve stir-fry sprinkled with nuts.

*per serving 19.6g total fat (3.1g saturated fat); 6.1g carbohydrate;
1221kJ (292 cal); 23g protein; 12.8g fibre*

ratatouille

preparation time 20 minutes
cooking time 25 minutes
serves 1

1 small red pepper (150g)
1 small yellow pepper (150g)
1 teaspoon olive oil
1 clove garlic, crushed
½ small red onion (50g), chopped coarsely
1 baby aubergine (60g), sliced thickly
1 small courgette (90g), sliced thickly
2 large tomatoes (440g), peeled, chopped coarsely
100g mushrooms, sliced thickly
1 tablespoon fresh lemon juice
1 tablespoon coarsely chopped fresh flat-leaf parsley

1 Quarter peppers; discard seeds and membranes. Roast under grill or in very hot oven, skin-side up, until skin blisters and blackens. Cover pepper pieces with plastic or paper for 5 minutes; peel away skin then chop flesh coarsely.
2 Meanwhile, heat oil in medium saucepan; cook garlic, onion, aubergine, courgette, tomato and mushroom, covered, over medium heat, stirring occasionally, 10 minutes. Stir in peppers; cook, uncovered, until heated through. Stir in juice and parsley.

per serving 6.2g total fat (0.7g saturated fat); 23.9g carbohydrate; 895kJ (214 cal); 14.3g protein; 13.9g fibre

roasted cherry tomatoes, broccoli and pepitas

preparation time 10 minutes
cooking time 20 minutes
serves 1

1 teaspoon olive oil
1 small red onion (100g), sliced thinly
2 cloves garlic, crushed
125g cherry tomatoes, halved
1 tablespoon cider vinegar
250g tenderstem broccoli
2 tablespoons toasted pepitas

1 Preheat oven to moderately hot (200°C/180°C fan-assisted).
2 Combine oil and onion in small baking dish; roast, uncovered, 10 minutes. Add garlic, tomato and vinegar; roast, uncovered, about 10 minutes or until tomato softens.
3 Meanwhile, boil, steam or microwave broccoli until tender; drain.
4 Serve brocolli topped with tomato mixture and seeds.

per serving 16.7g total fat (0.7g saturated fat); 10.3g carbohydrate; 1379kJ (330 cal); 14.2g protein; 17.9g fibre

stir-fried asian greens with mushrooms

preparation time 10 minutes
cooking time 5 minutes
serves 1

2 teaspoons sesame oil
1 clove garlic, crushed
10cm stick (20g) finely chopped fresh lemongrass
2cm piece fresh ginger (10g), grated
150g oyster mushrooms, chopped coarsely
150g button mushrooms, chopped coarsely
150g baby pak choy, chopped coarsely
¼ small chinese cabbage (175g), chopped coarsely

1 Heat oil in wok; stir-fry garlic, lemongrass, ginger and mushrooms until browned lightly. Add pak choy and cabbage; stir-fry until greens are just wilted.
2 Serve with lime wedges, if desired.

per serving 10.7g total fat (1.3g saturated fat); 7.4g carbohydrate; 757kJ (181 cal); 13.9g protein; 15.2g fibre

guacamole baked potato

preparation time 15 minutes
cooking time 1 hour
serves 1

1 medium potato (200g)
1 small avocado (200g)
½ small red onion (50g), chopped finely
1 small tomato (90g), deseeded, chopped finely
1 tablespoon finely chopped fresh coriander
1 tablespoon fresh lime juice
50g mixed salad leaves

1 Preheat oven to moderately hot (200°C/180°C fan-assisted). Pierce potato skin in several places with fork, wrap potato in foil; place on oven tray. Bake about 1 hour or until tender.
2 Mash avocado coarsely in small bowl; stir in onion, tomato, coriander and juice.
3 Cut a deep cross in potato; serve potato topped with guacamole accompanied with salad leaves.

per serving 32g total fat (6.9g saturated fat); 27.4g carbohydrate; 1818kJ (435 cal); 8.6g protein; 7.1g fibre

stir-fried tofu with lemongrass vegetables

preparation time 10 minutes
cooking time 5 minutes
serves 1

1 teaspoon sesame oil
100g firm tofu, diced into 1cm pieces
1 small red pepper (150g), sliced thinly
300g baby pak choy, chopped coarsely
10cm stick (20g) finely chopped fresh lemongrass
1 clove garlic, crushed
¼ cup loosely packed fresh coriander leaves

1 Heat oil in wok; stir-fry tofu, pepper, pak choy, lemongrass and garlic until vegetables are just tender. Stir in coriander.
2 Serve stir-fry with lemon wedges, if desired.

per serving 12.4g total fat (1.7g saturated fat); 9.7g carbohydrate; 924kJ (221 cal;) 17.7g protein; 8.2g fibre

aubergine with salsa fresca

preparation time 15 minutes
cooking time 15 minutes
serves 1

3 baby aubergines (180g), halved lengthways
SALSA FRESCA
½ small green pepper (75g), chopped finely
½ small yellow pepper (75g), chopped finely
1 small tomato (90g), deseeded, chopped finely
2 tablespoons finely shredded fresh basil
2 tablespoons fresh lemon juice

1 Cook aubergine on heated lightly oiled grill plate (or grill or barbecue) until tender.
2 Combine ingredients for salsa fresca in small bowl.
3 Serve grilled aubergine topped with salsa fresca.

per serving 0.8g total fat (0g saturated fat); 9.6g carbohydrate; 288kJ (69 cal); 4.6g protein; 5.9g fibre

black-eyed beans with sweet potato, shallots and garlic

preparation time 20 minutes (plus standing time)
cooking time 35 minutes
serves 1

⅓ cup (65g) dried black-eyed beans
1 teaspoon olive oil
5 shallots (125g)
5 cloves garlic, unpeeled
1 small sweet potato (250g), chopped coarsely
2 tablespoons fresh lemon juice
1 small radicchio, shredded finely
1 tablespoon finely chopped fresh flat-leaf parsley

1 Place beans in small bowl, cover with water; stand overnight, drain. Rinse under cold water; drain.
2 Preheat oven to moderately hot (200°C/180°C fan-assisted).
3 Combine oil, shallots, garlic and sweet potato on oven tray. Roast, uncovered, about 20 minutes or until garlic softens. Remove garlic from tray. Return remaining vegetables to oven; roast, uncovered, about 15 minutes or until vegetables are browned lightly.
4 Meanwhile, place beans in small saucepan of boiling water; bring to a boil. Reduce heat; simmer, covered, about 25 minutes or until beans are tender. Drain.
5 Using fingers, squeeze garlic from skins into medium bowl; stir in juice.
6 Add beans, vegetables, radicchio and parsley; toss gently to combine.

per serving 6.1g total fat (0.8g saturated fat); 39.1g carbohydrate; 1078kJ (258 cal); 10.3g protein; 12.1g fibre

brown rice with vegetables and tahini dressing

preparation time 15 minutes
cooking time 20 minutes
serves 1

¼ cup (50g) brown long-grain rice
1 small courgette (90g), sliced thinly
2 medium yellow patty-pan squash (60g), quartered
1 small carrot (70g), grated coarsely
¼ cup finely chopped fresh flat-leaf parsley
1 tablespoon sunflower seeds

TAHINI DRESSING
1 tablespoon tahini
2 teaspoons fresh lemon juice
1 tablespoon water
1 clove garlic, crushed

1 Cook rice in small saucepan of boiling water, uncovered, until rice is tender; drain.
2 Meanwhile, boil, steam or microwave courgette and squash, separately, until tender; drain.
3 Combine rice in small bowl with carrot, parsley and seeds.
4 Place ingredients for tahini dressing in screw-top jar; shake well.
5 Serve rice and vegetables drizzled with dressing.

per serving 24.4g total fat (2.7g saturated fat); 46.6g carbohydrate; 1965kJ (470 cal); 16g protein; 12.6g fibre

dhal with vegetables

preparation time 10 minutes
cooking time 35 minutes
serves 1

1 teaspoon vegetable oil
2cm piece fresh ginger (10g), grated
4cm piece fresh turmeric (20g), grated
1 clove garlic, crushed
½ cup (100g) yellow split peas
1 small carrot (70g), chopped coarsely
2 cups (500ml) water
1 small courgette (90g), chopped coarsely

GINGER YOGURT
1 tablespoon finely chopped fresh coriander
1cm piece fresh ginger (5g), grated
1 tablespoon fresh lime juice
2 tablespoons sheep's milk yogurt

1 Heat oil in medium saucepan; cook ginger, turmeric and garlic, stirring, until fragrant. Add peas, carrot and the water; bring to a boil. Reduce heat; simmer, covered, about 25 minutes or until peas are almost tender. Add courgette; cook, covered, about 5 minutes or until courgette is just tender.
2 Meanwhile, combine ingredients for ginger yogurt in small bowl.
3 Serve dhal with ginger yogurt.

per serving 10g total fat (0.8g saturated fat); 54.8g carbohydrate; 1764kJ (422 cal); 27.3g protein; 14.5g fibre

leek, goat's cheese and brown lentil bake

preparation time 15 minutes
cooking time 1 hour
serves 1

⅓ cup (65g) brown lentils
1 bay leaf
1 medium leek (350g), sliced thinly
2 tablespoons fresh lemon juice
2 cloves garlic, crushed
¼ cup (60ml) vegetable stock (page 50)
40g goat's cheese, crumbled
1 tablespoon coarsely chopped fresh chives

1 Preheat oven to moderate (180°C/160°C fan-assisted).
2 Combine lentils and bay leaf in small saucepan, cover with water; bring to a boil. Reduce heat; simmer, covered, about 10 minutes or until lentils are almost tender. Drain; discard bay leaf.
3 Combine lentils, leek, juice, garlic and stock in 3-cup (750ml) ovenproof dish. Bake, covered, about 40 minutes or until the leek is tender, stirring halfway through cooking.
4 Preheat grill.
5 Sprinkle lentil mixture with cheese; place under grill about 3 minutes or until cheese browns lightly. Sprinkle with chives.

per serving 7.6g total fat (4.2g saturated fat); 18.1g carbohydrate; 819kJ (196 cal); 13.2g protein; 9.8g fibre

roasted root vegetables with yogurt

preparation time 15 minutes
cooking time 35 minutes
serves 1

1 small parsnip (120g), chopped coarsely
100g celeriac, chopped coarsely
150g pumpkin, chopped coarsely
1 medium potato (200g), chopped coarsely
2 cloves garlic, crushed
1 teaspoon finely chopped fresh rosemary
2 teaspoons olive oil
½ small red pepper (75g), chopped finely
1 tablespoon coarsely chopped fresh chives
2 tablespoons goat's milk yogurt

1 Preheat oven to moderately hot (200°C/180°C fan-assisted).
2 Combine parsnip, celeriac, pumpkin, potato, garlic, rosemary and oil on oven tray. Roast, uncovered, about 35 minutes or until vegetables are tender. Add pepper and chives; toss gently to combine.
3 Serve vegetables topped with yogurt and lemon wedges, if desired.

per serving 12.2g total fat (2.8g saturated fat); 51.3g carbohydrate; 1542kJ (369 cal); 13.2g protein; 12.3g fibre

brown rice pilaf

preparation time 15 minutes
cooking time 1 hour
serves 1

1 small sweet potato (250g), chopped coarsely
cooking-oil spray
1½ cups (375ml) vegetable stock (page 50)
1 teaspoon olive oil
1 small brown onion (80g), chopped finely
1 clove garlic, crushed
1 trimmed celery stalk (100g), chopped finely
70g mushrooms, chopped coarsely
¾ cup (150g) brown medium-grain rice
1 tablespoon finely grated lemon rind
¼ cup loosely packed fresh flat-leaf parsley leaves

1 Preheat oven to moderate (180°C/160°C fan-assisted).
2 Place sweet potato on lightly oiled oven tray; spray with oil. Roast, uncovered, about 25 minutes or until sweet potato is tender.
3 Meanwhile, bring stock to a boil in small saucepan. Reduce heat; simmer, uncovered.
4 Heat oil in medium saucepan; cook onion, garlic and celery, stirring, until onion softens. Add mushroom and rice; cook, stirring, 2 minutes. Add stock, reduce heat; simmer, covered, about 50 minutes or until stock is absorbed and rice is tender. Stir in sweet potato, rind and parsley.

per serving 11.1g total fat (1.6g saturated fat); 161.4g carbohydrate; 3515kJ (841 cal); 22.2g protein; 18g fibre

chickpea patties with tomato and cucumber salad

preparation time 20 minutes (plus refrigeration time)
cooking time 40 minutes
serves 1

1 medium potato (200g)
300g can chickpeas, rinsed, drained
1 clove garlic, crushed
1 spring onion, sliced thinly
⅓ cup coarsely chopped fresh coriander
1 tablespoon polenta
½ cucumber (130g)
1 small plum tomato (60g), sliced thickly
1 tablespoon fresh lime juice
1 teaspoon pepitas
1 teaspoon sesame seeds
¼ cup (70g) sheep's milk yogurt

1 Boil, steam or microwave potato until tender; drain. Mash potato and chickpeas in medium bowl; stir in garlic, onion and coriander. Using hands; shape mixture into two patties. Coat with polenta; refrigerate 1 hour.
2 Cook patties in lightly oiled medium frying pan until browned lightly. Transfer to oven tray; bake in preheated moderate oven (180°C/160°C fan-assisted) about 15 minutes or until patties are heated through.
3 Meanwhile, slice half of the cucumber thinly; combine in medium bowl with tomato, juice and seeds. Cut remaining cucumber coarsely; combine in small bowl with yogurt. Serve patties with salad and yogurt.

per serving 21.1g total fat (1.4g saturated fat); 64.6g carbohydrate; 2491kJ (596 cal); 24.5g protein; 18.5g fibre

roasted vegetable stack

preparation time 10 minutes
cooking time 20 minutes
serves 1

1 baby fennel bulb (130g)
1 medium plum tomato (75g), halved lengthways
½ small red pepper (75g), sliced thickly
½ medium courgette (60g), sliced thickly lengthways
1 baby aubergine (60g), sliced thickly
cooking-oil spray
1 tablespoon finely chopped fresh flat-leaf parsley
1 tablespoon fresh lemon juice
1 teaspoon olive oil

1 Preheat oven to moderately hot (200°C/180°C fan-assisted).
2 Reserve fennel tips from fennel; slice fennel thinly.
3 Place vegetables on lightly oiled oven tray; spray with oil. Roast, uncovered, about 20 minutes until vegetables soften. Stir in half of the parsley.
4 Stack vegetables on serving plate; drizzle with combined juice and oil, sprinkle with remaining parsley and coarsely chopped reserved fennel tips.

per serving 7.2g total fat (0.8g saturated fat); 9.7g carbohydrate; 514kJ (123 cal); 4.1g protein; 6.5g fibre

oven-roasted ratatouille with almond gremolata*

preparation time 10 minutes
cooking time 40 minutes
serves 1

2 baby aubergines (120g), chopped coarsely
1 medium courgette (120g), chopped coarsely
1 small red pepper (150g), chopped coarsely
1 clove garlic, crushed
2 teaspoons olive oil
100g mushrooms, chopped coarsely
125g cherry tomatoes, halved

ALMOND GREMOLATA
2 tablespoons coarsely chopped fresh flat-leaf parsley
2 tablespoons coarsely chopped fresh basil
1 teaspoon finely grated lemon rind
2 tablespoons toasted slivered almonds, chopped coarsely
1 clove garlic, crushed

1 Preheat oven to moderately hot (200°C/180°C fan-assisted).
2 Combine aubergine, courgette, pepper, garlic and oil in small shallow baking dish. Roast, uncovered, 30 minutes, stirring occasionally. Add mushroom and tomato; roast, uncovered, about 10 minutes or until vegetables are just tender.
3 Meanwhile, combine ingredients for almond gremolata in small bowl.
4 Serve ratatouille topped with gremolata.

per serving 21.6g total fat (2.4g saturated fat); 16g carbohydrate; 1304kJ (312 cal); 13.8g protein; 14.2g fibre

before and after detox recipe

poached fish with herb salad*

preparation time 20 minutes
cooking time 10 minutes
serves 1

3 cups (750ml) water
2 cloves garlic, crushed
5cm piece fresh ginger (25g), sliced thinly
2 white fish fillets (220g)
1 lime, cut into wedges

HERB SALAD
¼ cup loosely packed fresh mint leaves
¼ cup loosely packed fresh coriander leaves
¼ cup loosely packed fresh basil leaves, torn
½ small red onion (50g), sliced thinly
½ cucumber (130g), deseeded, sliced thinly
1 tablespoon fresh lime juice
1cm piece fresh ginger (5g), grated

1 Place the water, garlic and ginger in medium frying pan; bring to a boil. Add fish, reduce heat; simmer, uncovered, about 5 minutes or until fish is cooked as desired. Remove fish with slotted spoon; discard liquid.
2 Meanwhile, combine ingredients for herb salad in medium bowl.
3 Serve fish with salad and lime wedges.

per serving 3g total fat (1g saturated fat);
8.3g carbohydrate; 1124kJ (269 cal); 49.6g protein;
6.6g fibre

before and after detox recipe

steamed asian bream*

preparation time 10 minutes
cooking time 15 minutes
serves 1

1 whole bream (240g)
3cm piece fresh ginger (15g), cut into matchsticks
1 spring onion, sliced thinly
1 small carrot (70g), cut into matchsticks
1 tablespoon tamari
1 teaspoon sesame oil

1 Preheat oven to moderately hot (200°C/180°C fan-assisted).
2 Lightly oil sheet of foil large enough to enclose fish. Place fish on foil, fill cavity with half of the vegetables. Brush fish with combined tamari and oil; top with remaining vegetables.
3 Fold edges of foil to enclose fish; place fish parcel on oven tray. Cook about 15 minutes or until fish is cooked as desired.
4 Serve fish sprinkled with fresh coriander leaves, if desired.

per serving 11.2g total fat (2.9g saturated fat);
5g carbohydrate; 957kJ (229 cal); 26.8g protein;
2.4g fibre

before and after detox recipe

vegetable and white bean stew*

preparation time 15 minutes
cooking time 30 minutes
serves 1

1 teaspoon olive oil
1 small leek (200g), sliced thinly
1 medium carrot (120g), sliced thickly
1 shallot (25g), chopped finely
2 cloves garlic, crushed
2 tablespoons rolled oats
1½ cups (375ml) water
2 tablespoons coarsely chopped fresh chives
½ cup (100g) canned white beans, rinsed, drained
2 teaspoons finely grated lemon rind
2 tablespoons sheep's milk yogurt

1 Heat oil in medium saucepan; cook leek, carrot, shallot and garlic, stirring, 10 minutes. Add oats and the water; bring to a boil. Reduce heat; simmer, covered, about 15 minutes or until liquid is almost absorbed. Stir in half of the chives.
2 Mash beans with rind and yogurt in small saucepan; cook, stirring, until heated through.
3 Serve stew topped with bean mixture and remaining chives.

per serving 9.2g total fat (0.9g saturated fat); 32.9g carbohydrate; 1120kJ (268 cal); 12.7g protein; 13.8g fibre

*before and after detox recipe

grilled fish fillet with gai larn*

preparation time 10 minutes
cooking time 10 minutes
serves 1

200g white fish fillet
200g gai larn, chopped coarsely
GINGER AND GARLIC DRESSING
2cm piece fresh ginger (10g), grated
1 clove garlic, crushed
1 tablespoon water
1 tablespoon tamari

1 Cook fish in heated lightly oiled small frying pan, uncovered, until cooked through.
2 Meanwhile, boil, steam or microwave gai larn until tender; drain.
3 Place ingredients for ginger and garlic dressing in screw-top jar; shake well.
4 Serve fish with gai larn, drizzle with dressing.

per serving 1.7g total fat (0.2g saturated fat); 3.5g carbohydrate; 828kJ (198 cal); 41.2g protein; 8.2g fibre

*before and after detox recipe

gi diet
plan

A diet low in fat (particularly saturated fat) and high in fresh unprocessed food, coupled with a reasonable amount of physical activity, is generally regarded as a straightforward and simple guide to a healthy life. Such a regime will not only help you maintain a proper weight, it can also help keep your cholesterol and blood pressure levels under control and assist in reducing the risk of heart disease and type-2 diabetes.

While genetics and lifestyle play a part in determining a person's weight, the fact remains that too many of us eat badly. Witness the growth in the takeaway and fast food industries, the increase in the percentage of people who can be classed as overweight or obese, and the growing incidence of type-2 diabetes and heart disease. High saturated-fat intakes have been linked not only to both of these diseases but to certain types of cancer as well.

food for living

In the distant past, our ancestors lived on a diet – consisting primarily of grains, cereals, fruits, vegetables, nuts and legumes – that was relatively low in saturated fat and high in foods that promoted activity. Our diet, however, has evolved into one in which saturated fats and overprocessed foods rule; it's a menu tailored to increase both our blood glucose (sugar) and insulin levels to worrying heights. Pressed for time and blessed with science, we rely heavily on foods that are quick to get to the table and don't need a lot of preparation. Worse, some manufactured and many takeaway foods use large quantities of fat to make bland carbohydrates exciting – think of deep-frying for potatoes.

CARBOHYDRATES

In tandem with lowering our saturated fat intakes, we should also concentrate on consuming more carbohydrates. Carbohydrate foods generally make us feel fuller faster than do fats, give us more energy, help stave off hunger pangs and do not easily convert to body fat. But what are they?

Carbohydrates come mostly from plants, ie., cereals and grains, fruits, vegetables and legumes, but dairy products also contain carbs. Recommended dietary guidelines suggest we eat substantial servings of cereals, legumes, rice and pasta, followed by vegetables and fruits. Dairy products should be eaten in moderation then, in diminishing quantities, meat, sugar, butter and the like can be consumed.

THE GLYCAEMIC INDEX

While a high-carbohydrate diet is better for us than a high-fat diet, certain kinds of carbohydrate foods are better than others. During the 1980s, nutritional research resulted in the creation of the glycaemic index (GI), a ranking of carbohydrates in foods based on their impact on blood glucose (sugar) levels in the body. Originally developed to help people with diabetes, research is showing that the glycaemic index is also a valid tool to assist in weight loss and heart disease prevention.

Rapidly absorbed pure glucose has the highest GI factor of 100. Carbohydrates that break down slowly and release glucose into the blood stream gradually have low GI values (55 or less), while those that are easily digested and absorbed quickly are considered to have high GI values (70 or more).

Medium (or intermediate) GI foods have values between 55 and 70. Low-fat high-GI food doesn't have to be excluded from a healthy diet when coupled with equal amounts of low-GI food – the result is a healthy diet with an intermediate-GI rating. The most important rule to follow is to eat as wide a variety as possible of low saturated-fat, low-to-medium GI foods.

Some food manufacturers have introduced a GI labelling system which indicates the glycaemic index rating of their products - look out for them next time you're in the supermarket.

SATURATED FAT

Eating too much saturated fat is bad for your health – it raises blood cholesterol more than other forms of fat and has far more kilojoules than carbohydrates or protein. High levels of saturated fat in the diet are linked to increased risk of heart and vascular disease, and certain cancers. The reason we consume saturated fat at all is because it is unavoidable in meat, many dairy products and some vegetable oils; its benefits are that it carries fat-soluble vitamins (A, D, E and K), it provides energy and supplies certain essential fatty acids needed to maintain the structure of cell membranes and form hormone-like substances that regulate the body's biochemistry. It is best for healthy adults to reduce daily consumption of saturated fats to less than 8% of total caloric intake. Saturated fats tend to be solid at room temperature and are found mainly in animal products such as butter, cream, chicken skin, fat on meat, cheese, lard and dripping. They are also found in pies and cakes, snack foods, pastries and oils such as palm and coconut.

WHY LOWER-GI MEANS A BETTER FUTURE

In simple terms, consumption of slowly digested carbohydrate foods (low GI) helps keep up energy levels and assists people with diabetes to manage their blood glucose levels which, in turn, aids their wellbeing and reduces the risk of health complications. High-GI foods are best consumed by athletes during periods of competition when rapid energy boosts are needed, or by people with diabetes when experiencing low blood glucose. It is wise to remember that many high-GI foods, such as potatoes, are useful sources of other essential nutrients such as dietary fibre, vitamins and minerals, and can be included in moderation in a healthy balanced diet.

Research also indicates that those consuming a high-GI diet have an increased risk of developing type-2 diabetes; diets with a low fibre intake and high-GI almost double that risk. Other indications are that high-GI diets can increase the risk of heart disease when measured in the context of other considerations such as age, sex, body weight, etc. Many experts believe that a lifestyle that works for people with diabetes – regular physical activity and a low saturated-fat, high-fibre diet – is good for the rest of us too. Another bonus of a high-carbohydrate lower-GI diet is the resulting reduction in calorie intake. You can use the GI factor as a guide to choosing foods for optimum weight management, high energy and more stable blood glucose levels. A balanced diet can include a wide array of foods, most of which are natural and wholesome. Simple changes to your diet, such as eating wholegrain rather than white bread, more fruit and lots of vegetables, will find you following a lower-GI eating plan without trying! The recipes in this book show you how to create low-fat dishes that are both healthy and delicious. As they are also low in saturated fats, they may also help assist in reducing blood cholesterol levels or lessen the risk of future illness.

> a lifestyle that works for people with diabetes . . . is good for the rest of us too.

GI TIPS FOR HEALTHY COOKING

- Don't cut or chop food too finely. This ensures you will receive the full benefit of the food's fibre content – the smaller the pieces of food, the less fibrous and the higher the GI rating
- Don't overprocess food
- Don't overcook food
- Acidulate food with vinegar or citrus juice
- Make use of a wide variety of grains and cereals, and vegetables and legumes – in as natural a state as possible
- Most fruit and semi-skimmed or skimmed milk or yogurt can be added to breakfast cereals to help lower overall GI
- Choose seeded or wholegrain breads over soft-textured plain-flour breads
- Eat basmati rice, sweet potato, or al dente pasta or noodles in preference to ordinary white potatoes and ordinary rice
- Add pulses and legumes, such as split peas, beans, lentils and chickpeas, to soups and casseroles

SODIUM

It's a given that we should all eat less salt (sodium); it can lead to increased blood pressure and the accompanying risk of heart disease and stroke. Still, sodium is essential in our diet – the recommended daily intake is 920mg to 2300mg, but this level can be achieved through the salt found naturally in fresh foods and unavoidably in manufactured foods. Try to choose processed foods that are labelled "no added salt" or "salt-reduced", and similarly try to avoid highly salted foods such as potato chips, salted nuts and most takeaway foods. Instead of using salt at the table, flavour your food with cracked pepper, chopped fresh herbs, lemon juice or balsamic vinegar, garlic, chilli and the like. Make your own mustard, tomato sauce, chutney and sweet chilli sauce _ without adding salt. Use dried ground spices, onions and leeks, wine and vinegar in cooking instead of salt.

LOWER-GI FOOD

- Basmati or gluten-free rice
- Al dente pasta
- Buckwheat, burghul, barley and bran
- Rolled oats and other rolled grains
- Grainy bread, fruit loaves
- Pitta, pumpernickel
- Carrots, sweet potatoes, peas and corn
- Chickpeas, kidney and cannellini beans
- Soy beans and other soy products
- Apples, pears and oranges
- Stone fruits (cherries, apricots and plums)
- Grapes, raisins and dried apricots
- Tomato soup, lentil soup
- Low-fat or non-fat milk and yogurt

HIGHER-GI FOOD

- Watermelon, dates, lychees
- White rice, white bread, white potatoes
- Sports drinks
- Waffles, pikelets and gluten-free pancakes made from mixes
- Pumpkin, broad beans and parsnips
- Bagels, rye bread, water biscuits
- Jelly beans and Fruit Roll-ups
- Frozen tofu and tapioca pudding made with milk

EAT YOUR VEGGIES!

An apple a day may keep the doctor away, but for keeping well and having a sense of wellbeing, turn to vegetables… five servings a day is the recommended amount. Recent studies indicate that phytochemicals (naturally occurring plant chemicals) and antioxidants (elements that stop free radicals from destroying DNA) contained in vegetables can play a part in reducing the possibility of cancer and heart disease.

- Eat more tomatoes (a good source of vitamin C), spinach (loaded with B vitamins, iron and folate) and broccoli (rich in fibre and calcium).
- Keep washed and trimmed celery, carrot, fennel, cucumber and the like in the refrigerator; you're more likely to snack on them if they're ready to eat. Juice vegetables when they look a little tired.
- Serve a green salad with every main meal – keep it simple so it's less of a chore to make. Use fresh lemon juice or balsamic vinegar and finely chopped herbs for a dressing.

FIBRE

Dietary fibre is mainly indigestible plant matter that has no nutritional value. Unable to be absorbed, it acts as roughage to help keep the digestive system healthy and filter excess cholesterol from digestive juices – essential in the maintenance of healthy gut bacteria. High-fibre carbohydrates as a rule have lower GI values and help assuage hunger pangs. A diet high in fibre is beneficial for people with type-2 diabetes and nutritionists advise that a healthy diet includes at least 30g of fibre daily. Good fibre sources are wholegrain cereals, brans and breads, and unpeeled, raw fruits and vegetables.

- Make fresh pasta sauces from vegetables – the Italians have for centuries. Broccoli or cauliflower florets, sugar snap peas or mangetout, chopped red onion, sliced mushrooms, cherry tomatoes or finely shaved fennel can be tossed into just-drained hot pasta and eaten immediately.
- Think about roasting or grilling your vegetables. Carrots, pumpkin, sweet potatoes, yams, turnips and beetroot can all be roasted in a hot oven and are perfectly delicious without adding anything to them. And aubergine, peppers, courgettes and whole red onions are delectable grilled on a hotplate or the barbecue.
- Don't forget how good homemade vegetable soup is, or how easy it is to make a vegetable stir-fry with lots of chilli, ginger and garlic.
- We are blessed with a wide variety of vegetables available in our supermarkets and greengrocers – so work your way through the huge selection. There's nothing wrong with eating the same old standards year in year out, but trying different vegetables can make meals more interesting. Select those in season when at their peak.

seven-day menu planner

1 DAY ONE

BREAKFAST
Rolled oat porridge
page 129
1 apple
1 slice wholegrain bread

LUNCH
Cottage cheese and
salad on 2 slices of
multigrain bread
1 orange

DINNER
Crisp-skinned snapper with
stir-fried vegetables and
black beans *page 171*
1 cup cooked brown rice

DESSERT
Apricot upside-down
cakes *page 209*

2 DAY TWO

BREAKFAST
2 crumpets with
unsaturated margarine
or marmite
1 small tub low-fat fruit
yogurt

LUNCH
Chilli and lime chicken
salad *page 142*
1 apple
2 slices wholegrain bread

DINNER
Lentil cottage pie
page 179
Green salad

DESSERT
Strawberry and rhubarb
muffins *page 209*

3 DAY THREE

BREAKFAST
Untoasted muesli
page 127
1 banana

LUNCH
1 cup canned peaches in
natural juice
1 small tub low-fat yogurt
(any flavour)
1 cup orange juice

DINNER
Rosemary, brie and
sun-dried tomato chicken
on corn mash *page 157*
Steamed broccoli and
carrots

DESSERT
Unsweetened small can
two fruits
1 scoop low-fat
ice-cream (any flavour)

4 DAY FOUR

BREAKFAST
Citrus compote *page 125*
2 slices toasted multigrain
bread with unsaturated
margarine

LUNCH
Sweet potato and
coriander soup *page 136*
1 wholemeal
bread roll

DINNER
Herb-crusted lamb racks
with potatoes and leek
page 154
Steamed brussels sprouts

DESSERT
Yogurt and mango jelly
page 197

5 DAY FIVE

BREAKFAST
Morning trifles *page 127*
2 slices toasted
wholemeal bread with
marmite or unsaturated
margarine

LUNCH
Rice and chickpea salad
page 147
1 pear

DINNER
Tofu stir-fry *page 175*

DESSERT
Chocolate brownie
page 201

6 DAY SIX

BREAKFAST
Strawberry hotcakes
with blueberry sauce
page 123

LUNCH
½ cup baked beans with
2 slices toasted wholegrain
bread
1 apple

DINNER
Grilled lean beef steak
1 jacket potato with
small tub low-fat natural
yogurt
Green salad
1 multigrain roll

DESSERT
Apricot strudel
page 193

7 DAY SEVEN

BREAKFAST
Breakfast with the lot
page 135
1 small tub low-fat fruit
yogurt

LUNCH
Niçoise salad *page 147*
1 orange
1 multigrain roll

DINNER
Pork loin with couscous
and apples *page 161*
Steamed baby potatoes
and green beans

DESSERT
2 scoops low-fat ice-cream
(any flavour)

juices and smoothies

fresh berry frappé

preparation time 5 minutes
makes 1 litre (4 cups)

300g blueberries
250g raspberries
4 cups crushed ice
1 cup (250ml) fresh orange juice

1 Blend berries until just smooth. Push berry puree through fine sieve into large bowl; discard solids in sieve.
2 Stir in ice and juice and spoon into serving glasses; serve immediately.
TIPS You can crush the ice in a blender or food processor. You can also use frozen berries for this recipe. Experiment with other berries – strawberries, blackberries, boysenberries – and adjust combinations to your taste.

per 250ml 0.4g fat; 338kJ (81 cal); 0g saturated fat; 17g carbohydrate; low GI

pineapple orange frappé

preparation time 5 minutes
makes 1 litre (4 cups)

1 medium pineapple (1.25kg), chopped coarsely
½ cup (125ml) orange juice
3 cups crushed ice
1 tablespoon finely grated orange rind

1 Blend pineapple and juice, in batches, until smooth.
2 Pour into large jug with crushed ice and rind; stir to combine. Serve immediately.

per 250ml 0.2g fat; 309kJ (74 cal); 0g saturated fat; 16g carbohydrate; low GI

mocha smoothie

preparation time 5 minutes
serves 4

1 litre (4 cups) skimmed milk
1 cup (250ml) low-fat chocolate mousse
1 cup (250ml) low-fat chocolate ice-cream
1 tablespoon instant coffee powder
½ teaspoon vanilla essence

1 Blend or process ingredients, in batches, until smooth. Serve immediately.

per serving 4g fat; 896kJ (214 cal); 0.9g saturated fat; 0.2g fibre; 19.3g carbohydrate; low GI

strawberry smoothie

preparation time 10 minutes
serves 4

200g low-fat frozen strawberry yogurt
250g strawberries
1 litre (4 cups) skimmed milk

1 Soften yogurt slightly; cut into pieces. Hull strawberries; cut each in half.
2 Blend or process ingredients, in batches, until smooth. Serve immediately.

per serving 3.5g fat; 783kJ (187 cal); 2.3g saturated fat; 1.4g fibre; 27g carbohydrate; low GI

peach smoothie

preparation time 10 minutes
serves 4

2 cups (500ml) skimmed soy milk
2 medium bananas (400g), chopped coarsely
4 medium peaches (600g), chopped coarsely
½ teaspoon ground cinnamon

1 Blend or process ingredients, in batches, until smooth. Serve immediately.

per serving 0.9g fat; 638kJ (152 cal); 0.1g saturated fat; 3.7g fibre; 29g carbohydrate; low GI

breakfast

strawberry hotcakes with blueberry sauce

preparation time 15 minutes
cooking time 20 minutes
serves 4

1 egg, separated
2 egg whites, extra
½ cup (125ml) apple sauce
1 teaspoon vanilla essence
2 cups (560g) low-fat plain yogurt
1¾ cups (280g) wholemeal self-raising flour
250g strawberries, hulled, chopped coarsely

BLUEBERRY SAUCE
150g blueberries, chopped coarsely
2 tablespoons sugar
1 tablespoon water

1 Using electric mixer, beat all egg whites in small bowl until soft peaks form.
2 Meanwhile, combine egg yolk, apple sauce, vanilla essence, yogurt, flour and strawberries in large bowl; fold in egg whites.
3 Pour ¼ cup batter into heated large lightly greased non-stick frying pan; using spatula, spread batter to shape into a round. Cook, over low heat, about 2 minutes or until bubbles appear on the surface. Turn hotcake; cook until lightly browned on other side. Remove from pan; cover to keep warm. Repeat with remaining batter. Serve with blueberry sauce.

BLUEBERRY SAUCE
Combine ingredients in small saucepan; bring to a boil, stirring constantly. Reduce heat; simmer 2 minutes. Remove from heat; cool. Blend or process blueberry mixture until smooth.

per serving 3.4g fat; 1639kJ (391 cal); 0.8g saturated fat; 10g fibre; 67g carbohydrate; medium GI

citrus compote

preparation time 20 minutes (plus standing time)
serves 4

2 large limes (160g)
3 large oranges (900g)
2 medium pink grapefruit (850g)
2 teaspoons sugar
½ vanilla pod, split
1 tablespoon small fresh mint leaves

1 Grate the rind of 1 lime and 1 orange finely; reserve grated rind. Peel remaining lime, remaining oranges, and grapefruit.
2 Segment all citrus over a large bowl to save juice, removing and discarding membrane from each segment. Add segments to bowl with sugar, vanilla pod and reserved rind; stir gently to combine.
3 Stand, covered, at room temperature 5 minutes; sprinkle with mint leaves.

per serving 0.7g fat; 685kJ (164 cal); 0g saturated fat; 6.7g fibre; 33.3g carbohydrate; low GI

rice porridge with raisins

preparation time 10 minutes
cooking time 30 minutes
serves 4

½ cup (100g) gluten-free rice
½ cup (125ml) water
2 cups (500ml) skimmed milk
1 tablespoon brown sugar
¼ cup (40g) raisins
pinch nutmeg
⅔ cup (160ml) skimmed milk, warmed, extra

1 Combine rice and the water in small saucepan; bring to a boil. Reduce heat; simmer, uncovered, until liquid is absorbed.
2 Add milk, sugar and raisins; simmer about 20 minutes or until rice is tender, stirring occasionally. Stir in nutmeg; serve warm with extra milk.

per serving 0.4g fat; 789kJ (188 cal); 0.2g saturated fat; 0.7g fibre; 38.6g carbohydrate; low GI

morning trifles

preparation time 20 minutes
serves 4

⅓ cup (20g) All-Bran
⅓ cup (20g) Special K
⅓ cup (20g) puffed wheat
250g strawberries, hulled
1 cup (280g) low-fat vanilla yogurt
⅓ cup (80ml) passionfruit pulp

1 Combine cereals in small bowl.
2 Cut six strawberries in half; reserve. Slice remaining strawberries thinly.
3 Divide half of the cereal mixture among four 1-cup (250ml) serving bowls; divide half of the yogurt, all the strawberry slices and half of the passionfruit pulp among bowls. Continue layering with remaining cereal and yogurt; top with reserved strawberry halves and remaining passionfruit pulp.
TIP You need about 5 passionfruit for this recipe.

per serving 0.7g fat; 527kJ (126 cal); 0.1g saturated fat; 6.4g fibre; 20.4g carbohydrate; low GI

untoasted muesli

preparation time 10 minutes
serves 6

2 cups (180g) rolled oats
½ cup (35g) All-Bran
1 tablespoon sunflower seed kernels
⅓ cup (55g) sultanas
¼ cup (35g) finely chopped dried apricots
½ cup (80g) finely chopped pitted dried dates
3 cups (750ml) skimmed milk
½ cup (140g) low-fat yogurt

1 Combine rolled oats, All-Bran, sunflower seed kernels and dried fruit in large bowl.
2 Divide the muesli and milk among serving bowls. Top with yogurt.
TIP You can use fruit juice, such as apple juice, instead of the milk, if you prefer.

per serving 4.1g fat; 1132kJ (270 cal); 0.7g saturated fat; 6.2g fibre; 47.3g carbohydrate; medium GI

rolled barley

rolled rice

rolled rye

rolled oats

rolled triticale

porridge with rolled grains

We used water to make these porridges, but no-fat milk or various fruit juices are an option, if desired.
The amounts given below for each type of porridge are enough to make 4 servings.

GRAIN	amount	soaking liquid	cooking liquid	cooking time	makes
ROLLED RICE	¾ cup (75g)	1½ cups (375ml)	¾ cup (180ml)	10 minutes	1¾ cups *per serving 0.5g fat;* *238kJ (57 cal);* *0g saturated fat; 0.6g fibre;* *14.8g carbohydrate*
ROLLED BARLEY	¾ cup (75g)	1½ cups (375ml)	¾ cup (180ml)	25 minutes	1½ cups *per serving 0.1g fat;* *276kJ (66 cal);* *0.1g saturated fat; 2.1g fibre;* *11.5g carbohydrate*
ROLLED OATS	¾ cup (60g)	1½ cups (375ml)	½ cup (125ml)	10 minutes	1½ cups *per serving 1.3g fat;* *233kJ (56 cal);* *0.2g saturated fat; 1g fibre;* *9.3g carbohydrate*
ROLLED RYE	¾ cup (75g)	1½ cups (375ml)	1½ cups (375ml)	50 minutes	1¾ cups *per serving 0.5g fat;* *248kJ (59 cal); 2.3g fibre;* *12.1g carbohydrate*
ROLLED TRITICALE	¾ cup (75g)	1½ cups (375ml)	1½ cups (375ml)	45 minutes	1¼ cups *per serving 0.5g fat;* *244kJ (58 cal);* *11.7g carbohydrate*

1 Place grain and soaking liquid in medium bowl, cover; stand at room temperature overnight.
2 Place undrained grain in medium saucepan; cook, stirring, until mixture comes to a boil.
Add cooking liquid, reduce heat; simmer, uncovered, for required cooking time.
3 Serve warm with toppings of your choice.

toppings

These toppings are enough for a single serving of porridge.

½ cup (125ml) skimmed milk	*0.1g fat; 189kJ (45 cal); 0.1g saturated fat; 0g fibre; 6.5g carbohydrate*
1 teaspoon honey	*0g fat; 94kJ (23 cal); 0g saturated fat; 0g fibre; 22.2g carbohydrate*
1 tablespoon low-fat vanilla yogurt	*0g fat; 68kJ (16 cal); 0g saturated fat; 0g fibre; 2.4g carbohydrate*
pinch cinnamon	*0g fat; 6kJ (2 cal)*
½ mashed banana	*0.1g fat; 240kJ (57 cal); 0g saturated fat; 5.1g fibre; 45.8g carbohydrate*
1 tablespoon dried fruit	*0.1g fat; 156kJ (37 cal); 0.1g saturated fat; 1.1g fibre; 13g carbohydrate*
2 teaspoons toasted shredded coconut	*2g fat; 79kJ (19 cal); 1.7g saturated fat; 0.4g fibre; 0.2g carbohydrate*

date and bran muffins

preparation time 15 minutes (plus standing time)
cooking time 25 minutes
makes 12 muffins

1½ cups (100g) unprocessed bran
1½ cups (375ml) skimmed milk
1¼ cups (185g) self-raising flour
½ cup (100g) firmly packed brown sugar
2 teaspoons ground cinnamon
⅓ cup (90g) low-fat dairy-free spread, melted
1 egg
1 cup (160g) finely chopped pitted dried dates

1 Preheat oven to moderate. Grease 12-hole (⅓ cup/80ml) muffin tray.
2 Combine bran and milk in large bowl; stand for 5 minutes.
3 Stir flour, sugar and cinnamon into bran mixture until combined. Add remaining ingredients; stir but do not overmix. Divide muffin mixture among holes of prepared tray.
4 Bake in moderate oven about 25 minutes. Turn muffins onto wire rack to cool.

per muffin 4.1g fat; 739kJ (177cal); 0.8g saturated fat; 5.7g fibre; 30.6g carbohydrate; high GI

buckwheat pancakes with lemon cream

preparation time 10 minutes
cooking time 10 minutes
serves 4

½ cup (75g) buckwheat flour
¼ cup (35g) wholemeal self-raising flour
1½ teaspoons baking powder
½ teaspoon ground cinnamon
2 egg whites
¾ cup (180ml) skimmed milk
1 tablespoon lemon juice
2 tablespoons maple syrup
20g low-fat dairy-free spread, melted
2 teaspoons coarsely grated lemon rind

LEMON CREAM
⅓ cup (80g) light soured cream
1 teaspoon finely grated lemon rind
1 teaspoon caster sugar

1 Sift flours, baking powder and cinnamon into medium bowl; gradually whisk in combined egg white, milk, juice and syrup. Stir spread into batter.
2 Pour ¼ cup batter into heated small lightly greased non-stick frying pan; cook about 2 minutes or until bubbles appear on the surface. Turn pancake; cook until lightly browned on other side. Remove from pan; cover to keep warm. Repeat with remaining batter. Serve with lemon cream; top with rind.

LEMON CREAM
Place ingredients in small bowl; stir until combined.

per serving 6g fat; 837kJ (200 cal); 3.3g saturated fat; 3.2g fibre; 28.5g carbohydrate; medium GI

corn fritters with roasted tomato chilli jam

preparation time 20 minutes
cooking time 1 hour 25 minutes
serves 4

1 cup (160g) wholemeal self-raising flour
½ teaspoon bicarbonate of soda
½ teaspoon hot paprika
¾ cup (180ml) skimmed milk
2 eggs, beaten lightly
2 cups (330g) fresh corn kernels
1 small red pepper (150g), chopped finely
2 spring onions, sliced thinly
2 tablespoons finely chopped fresh flat-leaf parsley

ROASTED TOMATO CHILLI JAM
2 medium tomatoes (380g)
1 small red onion (100g), chopped finely
1 clove garlic, crushed
2 teaspoons grated fresh ginger
¼ cup (60ml) lime juice
2 tablespoons brown sugar
2 red thai chillies, chopped finely

1 Sift flour, soda and paprika into medium bowl. Make well in centre of flour mixture, gradually whisk in combined milk and eggs until batter is smooth. Stir corn, pepper, onion and parsley into batter.
2 Pour ¼ cup batter into heated large lightly greased non-stick frying pan; using spatula, spread batter to shape into a round. Cook about 2 minutes each side or until fritter is lightly browned and cooked through, remove from pan; cover to keep warm. Repeat with remaining batter.
3 Serve with baby spinach leaves.

ROASTED TOMATO CHILLI JAM
Preheat oven to hot. Halve tomatoes; place, cut-side up, on lightly oiled oven tray. Roast, uncovered, in hot oven 30 minutes; chop tomato coarsely. Combine tomato with remaining ingredients in small saucepan, stirring over low heat until sugar dissolves; bring to a boil. Reduce heat; simmer, uncovered, about 40 minutes or until thickened.
TIPS You can make double the quantity of jam and keep it, covered, in the refrigerator for up to 4 weeks. You need 2 medium corn cobs, each weighing about 250g after being trimmed. Roasted tomato chilli jam is best made a day or two ahead to allow the flavours to develop.

per serving 5g fat; 1250kJ (299 cal); 1.2g saturated fat; 8.9g fibre; 48.4g carbohydrate; medium GI

breakfast with the lot

preparation time 10 minutes
cooking time 25 minutes
serves 4

2 large plum tomatoes (180g), quartered
4 eggs
4 slices multigrain bread
60g light ham
50g baby spinach leaves

1 Preheat oven to hot. Line oven tray with baking parchment.
2 Place tomato, cut-side up, on prepared tray; roast, uncovered, in hot oven about 25 minutes or until softened and lightly browned.
3 Meanwhile, place enough water in a large shallow non-stick frying pan to come halfway up the side; bring to a boil. Break eggs, one at a time, into small bowl, sliding each into pan; allow water to return to a boil. Cover pan, turn off heat; stand about 4 minutes or until a light film of egg white has set over each yolk.
4 Toast bread slices until lightly browned both sides.
5 Using a spatula, remove eggs, one at a time, from pan; place egg, still on slide, on absorbent-paper-lined saucer to blot up any poaching liquid. Serve toast topped with ham, spinach, egg then tomato.

per serving 7g fat; 680kJ (160 cal); 2g saturated fat; 2.1g fibre; 12g carbohydrate; medium GI

egg-white omelette

preparation time 10 minutes
cooking time 15 minutes
serves 4

150g light ham
200g button mushrooms, sliced thinly
12 egg whites
¼ cup finely chopped fresh chives
2 medium tomatoes (380g), chopped coarsely
½ cup (45g) coarsely grated low-fat cheddar cheese
8 slices wholemeal bread

1 Trim and discard any fat from ham; cut into thin strips. Cook in heated large non-stick frying pan, stirring, until lightly browned. Remove from pan. Cook mushrooms in same pan, stirring, until lightly browned.
2 Using electric mixer, beat 3 of the egg whites in small bowl until soft peaks form; fold in a quarter of the chives. Preheat grill. Pour egg-white mixture into heated lightly oiled non-stick 20cm frying pan; cook, uncovered, over low heat until just browned underneath. Place pan under preheated grill; cook until top just sets. Place a quarter of the tomato on one half of the omelette; return to grill, cook until tomato is hot and top is lightly browned. Gently place a quarter of each of the cheese, ham and mushroom on tomato half of omelette; fold over to enclose filling. Carefully transfer omelette to serving plate; cover to keep warm.
3 Repeat step 2 with remaining egg whites and fillings.
4 Toast bread until lightly browned both sides. Serve omelettes with toast.

per serving 6.3g fat; 1268kJ (303 cal); 1.7g saturated fat; 7.4g fibre; 33.1g carbohydrate; low GI

soups

sweet potato and coriander soup

preparation time 10 minutes
cooking time 35 minutes
serves 4

1 teaspoon rape-seed oil
2 medium leeks (700g), chopped coarsely
3 cloves garlic, quartered
2 medium sweet potatoes (800g), chopped coarsely
1 litre (4 cups) chicken stock
⅔ cup (160ml) light evaporated milk
⅓ cup finely chopped fresh coriander

1 Heat oil in large saucepan; cook leek and garlic, stirring, until leek softens. Add sweet potato; cook, stirring, 5 minutes. Add stock; bring to a boil. Reduce heat; simmer, covered, about 20 minutes or until sweet potato softens.
2 Blend or process soup, in batches, until smooth; return soup to same cleaned pan. Simmer, uncovered, until soup thickens slightly.
3 Stir in evaporated milk and coriander; stir over heat, without boiling, until heated through. Top with fresh coriander leaves, if desired.

per serving 2.9g fat; 880kJ (210 cal); 0.7g saturated fat; 6.8g fibre; 34.6g carbohydrate; low GI

beetroot soup

preparation time 10 minutes (plus refrigeration time)
cooking time 35 minutes
serves 4

1 teaspoon olive oil
1 small brown onion (80g), chopped coarsely
1 clove garlic, crushed
3 medium beetroot (500g), trimmed, chopped coarsely
1 medium apple (150g), cored, chopped coarsely
1 litre (4 cups) vegetable stock (see page 50)
½ cup (125ml) water
¼ cup (60ml) lemon juice
¼ teaspoon Tabasco sauce
¼ cucumber (65g), deseeded, chopped finely
½ small red onion (50g), chopped finely
1 tablespoon light soured cream

1 Heat oil in large saucepan; cook onion and garlic, stirring, until onion softens. Add beetroot, apple, stock and the water; bring to a boil. Reduce heat; simmer, covered, about 20 minutes or until beetroot is tender, stirring occasionally.
2 Blend or process soup, in batches, until smooth. Stir in juice and sauce; refrigerate, covered, until cold.
3 Serve chilled soup topped with combined remaining ingredients.

per serving 3.4g fat; 519kJ (124 cal); 1.4g saturated fat; 4.7g fibre; 17.2g carbohydrate; medium GI

curried chicken and courgette soup

preparation time 10 minutes
cooking time 25 minutes
serves 4

1 tablespoon low-fat dairy-free spread
1 medium brown onion (150g), chopped finely
1 clove garlic, crushed
1 teaspoon curry powder
½ cup (100g) gluten-free rice
340g chicken breast fillets, sliced thinly
2 cups (500ml) water
1 litre (4 cups) chicken stock
4 medium courgettes, grated coarsely

1 Melt spread in large saucepan; cook onion and garlic, stirring, until onion softens. Add curry powder; cook, stirring, until mixture is fragrant.
2 Add rice and chicken; cook, stirring, 2 minutes. Add the water and stock; bring to a boil. Reduce heat; simmer, covered, 10 minutes. Add courgette; cook, stirring, about 5 minutes or until chicken is cooked through.
TIP Basmati rice can be substituted for the gluten-free rice, if necessary.

per serving 6.7g fat; 1098kJ (262 cal); 2.1g saturated fat; 2.7g fibre; 25.7g carbohydrate; medium GI

chestnut mushroom and barley soup

preparation time 10 minutes
cooking time 55 minutes
serves 4

300g chestnut mushrooms, quartered
1 clove garlic, crushed
2 teaspoons soy sauce
2 teaspoons water
1 small brown onion (80g), chopped finely
1 litre (4 cups) chicken stock
1 litre (4 cups) water, extra
½ cup (100g) pearl barley
1 untrimmed stick celery (150g), chopped coarsely
2 small carrots (140g), chopped coarsely
½ teaspoon freshly ground black pepper

1 Cook mushrooms, garlic, soy sauce and the water in heated large non-stick frying pan until mushrooms soften.
2 Cook onion in heated lightly oiled large saucepan, stirring, until softened. Add stock and the extra water; bring to a boil. Add barley, reduce heat; simmer, covered, 30 minutes.
3 Add mushroom mixture to saucepan with remaining ingredients; cook, uncovered, about 20 minutes or until barley and vegetables are tender.

per serving 2.7g fat; 607kJ (145 cal); 0.7g saturated fat; 6.4g fibre; 21.7g carbohydrate; medium GI

gazpacho

preparation time 25 minutes (plus refrigeration time)
serves 4

3 cups (750ml) tomato juice
8 medium plum tomatoes (600g), chopped coarsely
1 medium red onion (170g), chopped coarsely
1 clove garlic, quartered
½ cucumber (130g), chopped coarsely
1 small red pepper (150g), chopped coarsely
2 teaspoons Tabasco

SALSA
4 spring onions, chopped finely
¼ cucumber (65g), seeded, chopped finely
½ small yellow pepper (75g), chopped finely
2 teaspoons olive oil
2 tablespoons finely chopped fresh coriander

1 Blend or process juice, tomato, red onion, garlic, coarsely chopped cucumber and red pepper, in batches, until pureed. Strain through sieve into large bowl; add Tabasco. Cover; refrigerate 3 hours.
2 Combine salsa ingredients in small bowl.
3 Serves bowls of soup topped with salasa.

per serving 2.6g fat; 560kJ (134 cal); 0.3g saturated fat; 5.2g fibre; 17.7g carbohydrate; low GI

light meals and snacks

chilli and lime chicken salad

preparation time 20 minutes (plus cooling time)
cooking time 10 minutes
serves 4

1 cup (250ml) water
1 cup (250ml) chicken stock
340g chicken breast fillets
1 small carrot (70g)
1 small red pepper (150g), sliced thinly
½ small chinese cabbage (200g), shredded finely
2 spring onions, chopped finely
¾ cup (60g) beansprouts
½ cup firmly packed fresh coriander leaves
100g watercress, trimmed

CHILLI LIME DRESSING
¼ cup (60ml) lime juice
2 tablespoons sweet chilli sauce
1 clove garlic, crushed
1 tablespoon oyster sauce
1 teaspoon sesame oil

1 Bring the water and stock to a boil in large saucepan. Reduce heat; add chicken, simmer about 10 minutes or until chicken is cooked through. Allow chicken to cool in cooking liquid before draining. Discard liquid; slice chicken thinly.
2 Meanwhile, halve carrot crossways, cut each half into 2mm-wide lengths; cut lengths into matchstick-thin strips.
3 Place chicken and carrot in large bowl with pepper, cabbage, onion, beansprouts, coriander and watercress; add chilli lime dressing, toss to combine.

CHILLI LIME DRESSING
Combine ingredients in screw-topped jar; shake well.

per serving 6.7g total fat (1.8g saturated fat); 751kJ (179 cal); 4g fibre; 7.2g carbohydrate; medium GI

oven-roasted potato wedges with tomato relish

preparation time 15 minutes
cooking time 40 minutes
serves 6

1kg large new potatoes
vegetable-oil spray
1 teaspoon salt
1 teaspoon freshly ground black pepper
4 medium tomatoes (760g), chopped finely
1 small brown onion (80g), chopped finely
2 tablespoons brown sugar
2 tablespoons red wine vinegar
1 teaspoon mustard powder

1 Preheat oven to very hot.
2 Halve potatoes lengthways; cut each half into wedges. Place wedges, in single layer, in large shallow baking dish; spray with oil, sprinkle with salt and pepper. Bake, uncovered, in very hot oven about 30 minutes or until browned and crisp, turning occasionally.
3 Meanwhile, heat tomato, onion, sugar, vinegar and mustard in medium saucepan; bring to a boil. Reduce heat; simmer, uncovered, about 30 minutes or until relish thickens. Serve potato wedges with relish.

per serving 1.2g fat; 954kJ (228 cal); 0.1g saturated fat; 4.5g fibre; 29.5g carbohydrate; high GI

herbed chicken rice paper rolls

preparation time 30 minutes (plus refrigeration time)
cooking time 5 minutes
serves 4

200g chicken tenderloins
1 tablespoon coarsely chopped fresh basil
1 tablespoon coarsely chopped fresh mint
1 tablespoon white wine vinegar
1 medium carrot (120g)
½ medium red pepper (100g)
¼ cucumber (65g), seeded
16cm-square rice paper sheets
2 tablespoons finely chopped roasted unsalted peanuts
1 tablespoon lime juice
2 tablespoons soy sauce
½ teaspoon grated fresh ginger

1 Combine chicken, basil, mint and vinegar in medium bowl, cover; refrigerate at least 10 minutes.
2 Meanwhile, cut carrot, pepper and cucumber into thin strips.
3 Cook chicken on heated lightly oiled grill plate (or grill or barbecue) until lightly browned all over and cooked through. Stand 5 minutes; slice thinly.
4 Using hands, dip rice paper sheets, one at a time, in medium bowl of warm water until just softened; dry carefully with absorbent paper. Divide chicken, carrot, pepepr and cucumber along centre of each rice paper sheet; scatter peanuts over filling. Roll rice paper sheets to enclose filling, folding in sides after first complete turn of roll. Serve rolls with dipping sauce made with combined remaining ingredients.

per serving 6.5g fat; 891kJ (213 cal); 1.4g saturated fat; 2.1g fibre; 22.5g carbohydrate; low GI

rice and chickpea salad

preparation time 15 minutes
cooking time 10 minutes (plus standing time)
serves 6

1 cup (200g) gluten-free rice
1¾ cups (430ml) water
300g can chickpeas, rinsed, drained
¼ cup (40g) sultanas
¼ cup (35g) dried apricots, chopped finely
2 spring onions, sliced thinly
2 tablespoons toasted pine nuts

BALSAMIC ORANGE DRESSING
1 teaspoon finely grated orange rind
⅓ cup (80ml) orange juice
1 tablespoon balsamic vinegar
1 clove garlic, crushed
1 teaspoon grated fresh ginger

1 Combine rice and the water in medium heavy-based saucepan; bring to a boil. Reduce heat; simmer, covered, about 8 minutes or until rice is tender. Remove from heat; stand, covered, 10 minutes. Fluff rice with fork; cool then refrigerate, covered, until cold.
2 Combine rice with remaining ingredients in large bowl; add balsamic orange dressing, toss gently to combine.

BALSAMIC ORANGE DRESSING
Combine ingredients in screw-topped jar; shake well.
TIP You can use basmati rice instead of gluten-free, if necessary.

per serving 4.3g fat; 929kJ (222 cal); 0.2g saturated fat; 2.1g fibre; 26.7g carbohydrate; low GI

niçoise salad

preparation time 15 minutes
cooking time 5 minutes
serves 4

100g green beans, trimmed
2 x 180g cans tuna in springwater, drained
1 small red onion (100g), sliced thinly
2 spring onions, sliced thinly
250g cherry tomatoes, halved
100g mixed salad leaves
2 teaspoons finely grated lemon rind
½ cup (125ml) lemon juice
1 tablespoon wholegrain mustard
2 cloves garlic, crushed
2 teaspoons sugar

1 Boil, steam or microwave beans until just tender; cool. Cut beans in half.
2 Combine beans with tuna, onions, tomato and salad leaves in large bowl.
3 Whisk remaining ingredients in small bowl; add to salad, toss gently to combine.
TIP For additional protein, you may wish to add a hard-boiled egg per person (see cover image).

per serving 2.3g fat; 568kJ (136 cal); 0.7g saturated fat; 3.1g fibre; 7.3g carbohydrate; low GI

tofu cakes with sweet chilli dipping sauce

preparation time 15 minutes (plus standing time)
cooking time 15 minutes
makes 20 tofu cakes

300g fresh firm tofu
1 cup (150g) cooked basmati rice
3 teaspoons red curry paste
2 spring onions, chopped finely
1 tablespoon coarsely chopped fresh coriander
1 egg, beaten lightly

SWEET CHILLI DIPPING SAUCE
¼ cup (60ml) white vinegar
½ cup (110g) caster sugar
½ teaspoon salt
¾ cup (180ml) water
½ small red onion (50g), chopped finely
½ small carrot (35g), chopped finely
¼ cucumber (65g), deseeded, chopped finely
2 tablespoons coarsely chopped fresh coriander
⅓ cup (80ml) sweet chilli sauce

1 Press tofu between two chopping boards or trays, place weight on top; elevate boards slightly to allow tofu liquid to drain away. Stand 20 minutes; chop coarsely. Blend or process tofu until smooth.

2 Preheat oven to moderately hot; line oven tray with baking parchment.

3 Combine tofu in medium bowl with rice, paste, onion, coriander and egg.

4 Shape level tablespoons of the tofu mixture into rounds; place on oven tray. Bake, uncovered, in moderately hot oven about 10 minutes or until lightly browned and heated through. Serve tofu cakes with sweet chilli dipping sauce.

SWEET CHILLI DIPPING SAUCE
Place vinegar, sugar, salt and the water in small saucepan; bring to a boil. Boil, stirring, about 2 minutes or until sugar dissolves. Pour vinegar mixture over remaining ingredients in medium heatproof bowl; stir to combine.

TIP You need to cook about ⅓ cup basmati rice for this recipe.

per cake 1.7g fat; 326kJ (78 cal); 0.3g saturated fat; 0.8g fibre; 12.9g carbohydrate; medium GI

lamb and tabbouleh wrap

preparation time 35 minutes
cooking time 10 minutes
makes 8 wraps

1 cup (250ml) water
½ cup (80g) bulghur wheat
300g can chickpeas, drained, rinsed
⅓ cup (95g) low-fat plain yogurt
1 teaspoon finely grated lemon rind
1 tablespoon lemon juice
3 spring onions, sliced thinly
2 medium tomatoes (380g), deseeded, chopped finely
½ cucumber (130g), deseeded, chopped finely
1 cup coarsely chopped fresh flat-leaf parsley
½ cup coarsely chopped fresh mint
1 tablespoon lemon juice, extra
250g lean lamb strips
2 tablespoons sumac
8 tortilla wraps

1 Combine the water and bulghur wheat in small bowl; stand 30 minutes. Drain; squeeze bulghur wheat with hands to remove excess water.
2 Meanwhile, blend or process chickpeas, yogurt, rind and juice until hummus is smooth.
3 Combine bulghur wheat in large bowl with onion, tomato, cucumber and herbs; add extra juice, toss gently until tabbouleh is combined.
4 Toss lamb in sumac; cook, in batches, on heated lightly oiled grill plate (or grill or barbecue) until browned both sides and cooked as desired.
5 Just before serving, spread hummus equally over half of each slice of the bread, top with equal amounts of lamb and tabbouleh; roll to enclose filling. Cut into pieces, if desired, to serve.
TIP Sumac, a purple-red astringent spice, can be found at any Middle-Eastern food store.

per wrap 4.9g fat; 1304kJ (311 cal); 1.4g saturated fat; 7.7g fibre; 48.4g carbohydrate; medium GI

chicken tikka wrap

preparation time 20 minutes (plus refrigeration time)
cooking time 15 minutes
serves 4

2 single chicken breast fillets (340g)
1 tablespoon tikka masala curry paste
2½ cups (700g) low-fat plain yogurt
1 cucumber (260g), deseeded, chopped finely
⅓ cup coarsely chopped fresh mint
1 small red onion (100g), chopped finely
4 large pitta breads
100g mixed salad leaves

1 Cut each chicken fillet in half horizontally. Combine chicken in large bowl with paste and 2 tablespoons of yogurt, cover; refrigerate 3 hours or overnight.
2 Cook chicken, in batches, on heated lightly oiled grill plate (or grill or barbecue) until browned all over and cooked through. Stand 5 minutes; slice thinly.
3 Meanwhile, combine cucumber, mint, onion and remaining yogurt in medium bowl.
4 Just before serving, spread yogurt mixture over whole of each piece of bread; top with equal amounts of salad leaves then chicken. Roll to enclose filling.

per serving 6.3g fat; 1248kJ (298 cal); 1.7g saturated fat; 2.9g fibre; 25.3g carbohydrate; medium GI

beef and bean tacos

preparation time 15 minutes
cooking time 20 minutes
serves 4

1 clove garlic, crushed
80g lean minced beef
½ teaspoon chilli powder
¼ teaspoon ground cumin
300g can kidney beans, rinsed, drained
2 tablespoons tomato paste
½ cup (125ml) water
1 medium tomato (190g), chopped coarsely
4 taco shells
¼ small iceberg lettuce, shredded finely

SALSA CRUDA
¼ cucumber (65g), seeded, chopped finely
½ small red onion (40g), chopped finely
1 small tomato (130g), seeded,chopped finely
1 teaspoon mild chilli sauce

1 Preheat oven to moderate.
2 Heat large lightly oiled non-stick frying pan; cook garlic and beef, stirring, until beef is browned all over. Add chilli, cumin, beans, paste, the water and tomato; cook, covered, over low heat about 15 minutes or until mixture thickens slightly.
3 Meanwhile, toast taco shells, upside-down and uncovered, on oven tray in moderate oven for around 5 minutes.
4 Just before serving, fill taco shells with beef mixture, lettuce and salsa cruda.

SALSA CRUDA
Combine ingredients in small bowl.

per serving 4.6g fat; 654kJ (156 cal); 1g saturated fat; 6.8g fibre; 18.4g carbohydrate; medium GI

roasted ratatouille with rye toast

preparation time 15 minutes
cooking time 20 minutes
serves 4

4 baby aubergines (240g), chopped coarsely
3 small courgettes (270g), chopped coarsely
100g button mushrooms, chopped coarsely
250g cherry tomatoes, halved
1 small leek (200g), chopped coarsely
2 cloves garlic, crushed
1 tablespoon olive oil
½ cup coarsely chopped fresh basil
1 tablespoon finely chopped fresh oregano
2 tablespoons balsamic vinegar
4 thick slices dark rye bread, toasted

1 Preheat oven to hot.
2 Combine aubergine, courgette, mushrooms, tomato, leek, garlic and oil in large shallow baking dish; roast, uncovered, in hot oven, stirring occasionally, about 20 minutes or until vegetables are tender.
3 Stir basil, oregano and vinegar into ratatouille.
4 Serve warm on rye bread.

per serving 6.2g fat; 766kJ (183 cal); 0.8g saturated fat; 8.1g fibre; 24.2g carbohydrate; high GI

main courses

herb-crusted lamb racks with potatoes and leek

preparation time 25 minutes
cooking time 55 minutes (plus standing time)
serves 4

4 x 3-cutlet racks of lamb (900g)
¼ cup (20g) fresh white breadcrumbs
1 tablespoon finely chopped fresh rosemary
1 tablespoon finely chopped fresh flat-leaf parsley
2 teaspoons finely chopped fresh thyme
3 cloves garlic, crushed
3 teaspoons bottled coriander pesto
1kg salad potatoes, halved lengthways
vegetable-oil spray
1 teaspoon sea salt
2 medium leeks (700g), trimmed
2 teaspoons low-fat dairy-free spread
¼ cup (60ml) chicken stock
¼ cup (60ml) dry white wine

1 Preheat oven to moderately hot.
2 Remove any excess fat from lamb. Combine breadcrumbs, herbs, garlic and pesto in small bowl. Using hands, press breadcrumb mixture onto lamb racks, cover; refrigerate until required.
3 Place potato in large shallow baking dish; spray with oil, sprinkle with salt. Roast, uncovered, in moderately hot oven 20 minutes.
4 Place lamb on top of the potato; roast, uncovered, in moderately hot oven 10 minutes. Reduce heat to slow; cook about 20 minutes or until potato is tender and lamb is cooked as desired.
5 Meanwhile, cut leeks into 10cm lengths; slice thinly lengthways. Melt spread in large frying pan; cook leek, stirring, until leek softens. Stir in stock and wine; bring to a boil. Reduce heat; simmer, uncovered, until liquid reduces by half.
6 Stand lamb 5 minutes before cutting racks into cutlets; serve cutlets with potato and leek.

per serving 13.7g fat; 1829kJ (437 cal); 5.6g saturated fat; 7.9g fibre; 40.1g carbohydrate; high GI

rosemary, brie and sun-dried tomato chicken on corn mash

preparation time 30 minutes
cooking time 15 minutes
serves 4

30g sun-dried tomatoes, chopped finely
1 tablespoon finely chopped fresh rosemary
4 single chicken breast fillets (680g)
60g firm brie, quartered
1kg medium new potatoes, quartered
2 cloves garlic, crushed
2 tablespoons skimmed milk
2 tablespoons light soured cream
310g can creamed corn

1 Combine tomato and rosemary in small bowl.
2 Using small sharp knife, slit a pocket in one side of each fillet, taking care not to cut all the way through. Divide tomato mixture and brie among pockets; secure openings with toothpicks.
3 Cook chicken on heated lightly oiled grill plate (or grill or barbecue) until browned both sides and cooked through; cover to keep warm.
4 Meanwhile, boil, steam or microwave potato until tender; drain. Mash potato in large bowl with garlic, milk and sour cream; fold in corn. Serve chicken with mash.
TIPS If sun-dried tomatoes are too dry, reconstitute in hot water; drain before mixing with the rosemary. You can substitute the corn with 125g of wilted baby spinach leaves, if desired.

per serving 15g fat; 2124kJ (508 cal); 6g saturated fat; 7.5g fibre; 44.5g carbohydrate; high GI

tarragon chicken with carrot mash and leek

preparation time 20 minutes (plus refrigeration time)
cooking time 25 minutes
serves 4

4 chicken breast fillets (680g), sliced thickly
1 tablespoon finely chopped fresh tarragon
1 tablespoon wholegrain mustard
2 tablespoons low-fat dairy-free spread
2 large leeks (500g), trimmed, chopped finely
4 medium carrots (480g), chopped coarsely
1½ cups (375ml) chicken stock
pinch nutmeg

1 Thread equal amounts of chicken onto each of 12 skewers. Using fingers, press combined tarragon and mustard all over chicken, cover skewers; refrigerate 30 minutes.
2 Meanwhile, melt spread in large non-stick frying pan; cook leek, stirring, until softened. Cover to keep warm.
3 Preheat oven to moderately hot. Boil or microwave carrot in chicken stock until just tender; drain in strainer over small bowl. Reserve ½ cup of the cooking liquid; discard the remainder. Blend or process carrot with nutmeg until pureed. Cover to keep warm.
4 Cook chicken and reserved liquid in large shallow baking dish, uncovered, in moderately hot oven about 15 minutes or until cooked through.
5 Divide carrot mash among serving plates; top with chicken and leek.
TIPS You need 12 bamboo skewers for this recipe; soak them in water for at least an hour before using to avoid them splintering or scorching.

per serving 13.9g fat; 1335kJ (319 cal); 1.4g saturated fat; 9g fibre; 76.8g carbohydrate; low GI

grilled chicken with barley pilaf

preparation time 10 minutes
cooking time 55 minutes
serves 4

1 cup (215g) pearl barley
2 cups (500ml) water
2 cups (500ml) chicken stock
250g cherry tomatoes
150g yellow cherry tomatoes
4 chicken breast fillets (680g)
½ teaspoon coarsely ground black pepper
½ cup coarsely chopped fresh basil
2 spring onions, sliced thinly
1 tablespoon dijon mustard

1 Preheat oven to hot.
2 Cook barley with the water and stock in medium pan, uncovered, over low heat, about 50 minutes or until most of the liquid is absorbed, stirring occasionally.
3 Meanwhile, roast tomatoes in hot oven on baking-parchment-lined oven tray, uncovered, about 20 minutes or until just browned and softened.
4 Cook chicken on heated lightly oiled grill plate (or grill or barbecue) until browned both sides and cooked through.
5 Stir tomatoes, pepper, basil and onion gently into barley. Serve chicken, dolloped with mustard, with pilaf.
TIP If tomatoes are too large, halve before roasting.

per serving 11.3g fat; 1726kJ (412 cal); 3.4g saturated fat; 7.7g fibre; 34.2g carbohydrate; low GI

fried rice

preparation time 10 minutes
cooking time 10 minutes
serves 4

2 teaspoons groundnut oil
1 medium brown onion (150g), chopped coarsely
2 cloves garlic, crushed
2 teaspoons grated fresh ginger
300g lean minced pork
1 untrimmed stick celery (150g), sliced thickly
1 small red pepper (150g), chopped coarsely
1 large courgette (150g), chopped coarsely
4 cups (600g) cooked basmati rice
¾ cup (90g) frozen peas, thawed
¼ cup (60ml) soy sauce
2 spring onions, sliced thinly

1 Heat oil in wok or large non-stick frying pan; stir-fry brown onion, garlic and ginger until onion has just softened. Add pork; stir-fry until brown and cooked through.
2 Add celery, pepper and courgette; stir-fry until just tender. Add rice, peas and sauce; stir-fry until hot. Toss spring onion through fried rice just before serving.
TIP You need to cook about 1½ cups of rice for this recipe. Cold rice, cooked the day before you intend to prepare the recipe, is best for this dish; the individual grains remain separate from one another and won't get mushy when reheated in the wok. Spread the cooked rice on a tray and allow to cool before covering and refrigerating overnight.

per serving 8.2g fat; 1527kJ (365 cal); 2.4g saturated fat; 4.2g fibre; 19.6g carbohydrate; medium GI

pork loin with couscous and apples

preparation time 35 minutes
cooking time 1 hour
serves 4

1 cup (200g) couscous
1 cup (250ml) boiling water
⅓ cup (55g) pitted prunes, chopped finely
1 tablespoon toasted pine nuts
2 tablespoons coarsely chopped fresh coriander
¼ cup coarsely chopped fresh flat-leaf parsley
500g rindless, boneless pork loin
2½ cups (625ml) cider
2 medium apples (300g), peeled, cored, sliced thickly
1 large red onion (300g), cut into thick wedges
2 tablespoons brown sugar

1 Preheat oven to moderately hot.
2 Combine couscous with the water in medium heatproof bowl, cover; stand about 5 minutes or until water is absorbed, fluffing with fork occasionally. Using fork, toss prunes, nuts, coriander and parsley into couscous.
3 Remove any excess fat from pork. Place pork on board, upside-down; slice through thickest part of pork horizontally, without cutting through at the other side. Open pork out to form one large piece; press 1 cup of the couscous mixture against loin along width of pork. Roll pork to enclose stuffing, securing with kitchen string at 2cm intervals.
4 Place rolled pork on rack in large shallow flameproof baking dish; pour 2 cups of the cider over pork. Roast, uncovered, in moderately hot oven about 50 minutes or until cooked through. Remove pork from baking dish; cover to keep warm.
5 Place remaining couscous mixture in small ovenproof dish; cook, covered, in moderately hot oven about 10 minutes or until heated through.
6 Meanwhile, heat pan juices in baking dish on top of stove; add remaining cider, apple, onion and sugar. Cook, stirring, until apple is just tender. Serve sliced pork with apple mixture and couscous.
TIPS We used Granny Smith apples in this recipe.
To simplify making this recipe, ask your butcher to remove any excess fat and butterfly the pork for you.

per serving 8.1g fat; 3044kJ (727 cal); 2g saturated fat; 4.6g fibre; 111.1g carbohydrate; low GI

beef, red wine and chilli casserole with polenta

preparation time 15 minutes
cooking time 1 hour 45 minutes
serves 4

2 teaspoons low-fat dairy-free spread
1.5kg lean beef braising steak, cut into 3cm pieces
2 cloves garlic, crushed
3 red thai chillies, deseeded, sliced thinly
2 teaspoons dijon mustard
1 large brown onion (200g), sliced thickly
2 medium tomatoes (380g), chopped coarsely
410g can tomato puree
¾ cup (180ml) dry red wine
½ cup (125ml) beef stock
1.125 litres (4½ cups) water
1 cup (170g) polenta
¼ cup (20g) finely grated parmesan cheese
2 tablespoons coarsely chopped fresh
flat-leaf parsley

1 Melt spread in large saucepan; cook beef, in batches, until browned all over. Cook garlic, chilli, mustard and onion in same pan, stirring, until onion softens. Return beef to pan with tomato; cook, stirring, 2 minutes.
2 Add puree, wine, stock and ½ cup of the water to pan; bring to a boil. Reduce heat; simmer, covered, about 1 hour 30 minutes or until beef is tender, stirring occasionally.
3 Meanwhile, bring the remaining litre of water to a boil in medium saucepan. Add polenta; cook, stirring, over medium heat about 10 minutes or until thickened. Stir cheese into polenta.
4 Stir parsley into beef casserole just before serving with polenta.
TIP As long as the wine you use is good enough to drink with the meal, any dry red will suffice; however, in keeping with the Italian feel of this recipe, we used a Chianti.

per serving 14.3g fat; 2058kJ (492 cal); 6.2g saturated fat; 3.7g fibre; 26.7g carbohydrate; low GI

thai lamb salad

preparation time 20 minutes (plus standing time)
cooking time 10 minutes
serves 4

100g bean thread noodles
500g lamb fillets, trimmed
1 medium red onion (170g), sliced thinly
3 spring onions, sliced thinly
1 cup (80g) beansprouts
1 cup loosely packed fresh coriander leaves
1 cup loosely packed fresh mint leaves
1 cup loosely packed fresh vietnamese mint leaves
½ cucumber (130g), deseeded, sliced thinly
2 red thai chillies, sliced thinly
200g cherry tomatoes, halved
2 cloves garlic, crushed
1 tablespoon finely chopped fresh lemongrass
⅓ cup (80ml) lime juice
1 tablespoon fish sauce
1 tablespoon soy sauce

1 Place noodles in medium heatproof bowl; cover with boiling water. Stand until just tender; drain. Rinse noodles under cold water; drain well.
2 Cook lamb on heated lightly oiled grill plate (or grill or barbecue) until browned and cooked as desired. Stand 5 minutes; slice thinly.
3 Meanwhile, combine onions, sprouts, herbs, cucumber, chilli and tomato in large bowl. Add lamb and combined remaining ingredients; toss to combine. Serve salad with noodles.

per serving 4.9g fat; 997kJ (238 cal); 2g saturated fat; 5.9g fibre; 18.3g carbohydrate; low GI

pork vindaloo

preparation time 15 minutes (plus standing time)
cooking time 50 minutes
serves 4

2 large brown onions (400g), chopped coarsely
5 cloves garlic, quartered
1 teaspoon ground cardamom
½ teaspoon ground clove
1 teaspoon ground cinnamon
2 teaspoons ground cumin
2 teaspoons ground turmeric
2 teaspoons cracked black pepper
3 red thai chillies, quartered
2 teaspoons black mustard seeds
1 tablespoon grated fresh ginger
⅓ cup (80ml) white vinegar
1kg pork fillet, trimmed
1 tablespoon vegetable oil
1 large brown onion (200g), sliced thinly
2 tablespoons tamarind paste
2 large tomatoes (500g), chopped coarsely
2 cups (400g) jasmine rice

1 Blend or process chopped onion, garlic, spices, chilli, seeds, ginger and vinegar to a smooth paste.
2 Trim any excess fat from pork; cut into 3cm pieces. Combine pork with a quarter of the curry paste in medium bowl; stir to coat pork all over. Cover; refrigerate 3 hours or overnight. Reserve remaining curry paste.
3 Heat oil in large saucepan; cook sliced onion, stirring, until just soft. Add reserved curry paste; cook, stirring, over low heat 5 minutes. Add pork; cook, stirring, about 5 minutes or until pork changes colour. Stir in tamarind paste and tomato; bring to a boil. Reduce heat; simmer, covered, about 40 minutes or until pork is tender and cooked through.
4 Meanwhile, cook rice in large saucepan of boiling water, uncovered, until just tender; drain. Serve curry on rice.
TIPS Vindaloo curry paste can be made up to a week ahead and kept, covered tightly, in the refrigerator. Making this dish a day ahead helps to intensify the flavours.

per serving 11.6g fat; 3159kJ (755 cal); 2.7g saturated fat; 6.5g fibre; 94.4g carbohydrate; medium GI

risoni marinara

preparation time 15 minutes
cooking time 25 minutes
serves 4

12 large uncooked prawns (600g)
12 small mussels (200g)
300g squid hoods
2 teaspoons olive oil
1 large brown onion (200g), chopped finely
2 cloves garlic, crushed
1 large red pepper (350g), sliced thinly
375g risoni
1½ cups (375ml) water
1½ cups (375ml) chicken stock
½ cup (125ml) dry white wine
pinch saffron threads
1 cup (125g) frozen peas, thawed
1 large tomato (250g), deseeded, sliced thinly

1 Shell and devein prawns, leaving tails intact. Scrub mussels; remove beards. Cut squid down centre to open out, score the inside in a diagonal pattern then cut into strips.
2 Heat oil in large saucepan; cook onion, garlic and pepper, stirring, about 3 minutes or until onion softens. Add risoni; stir to coat in onion mixture.
3 Stir in the water, stock, wine and saffron; bring to a boil. Reduce heat; simmer, uncovered, until liquid is absorbed and risoni is just tender, stirring occasionally.
4 Add prawns, mussels, squid, peas and tomato; cook, covered, until prawns are changed in colour and mussels have opened (discard any that do not).
TIP Risoni is a small, rice-sized pasta often used in Italian soups; any small soup pasta can be used instead of risoni for this recipe.

per serving 6.5g fat; 2488kJ (594 cal); 1.4g saturated fat; 9g fibre; 76.8g carbohydrate; low GI

oven-steamed ocean trout

preparation time 10 minutes
cooking time 15 minutes
serves 4

4 x 200g ocean trout fillets
2 tablespoons lemon juice
1 tablespoon drained capers, chopped coarsely
2 teaspoons coarsely chopped fresh dill
1.2kg large new potatoes, sliced thickly

1 Preheat oven to moderately hot.
2 Place each fillet on a square of foil large enough to completely enclose fish; top each fillet with equal amounts of juice, capers and dill. Gather corners of foil squares together above fish, twist to close securely.
3 Place parcels on oven tray; cook in moderately hot oven about 15 minutes or until fish is cooked as desired. Unwrap and remove fish from foil before serving.
4 Meanwhile, boil, steam or microwave potato until tender. Serve fish with potato.
TIP Use tweezers to remove any bones from fish.

per serving 7.9g fat; 1751kJ (418 cal); 1.8g saturated fat; 5.8g fibre; 39g carbohydrate; high GI

cajun-spiced fish with roasted corn salsa

preparation time 15 minutes
cooking time 25 minutes
serves 4

1 clove garlic, crushed
1 tablespoon low-fat dairy-free spread, melted
2 teaspoons sweet paprika
½ teaspoon ground cumin
1 teaspoon ground white pepper
¼ teaspoon cayenne pepper
4 x 200g firm white fish fillets
3 trimmed fresh corn cobs (750g)
1 small red onion (100g), chopped coarsely
1 medium avocado (250g), chopped coarsely
250g cherry tomatoes, halved
2 tablespoons lime juice
¼ cup coarsely chopped fresh coriander

1 Preheat oven to hot.
2 Combine garlic and spread in small jug; combine spices in small bowl.
3 Place fish on oven tray, brush both sides with garlic mixture, sprinkle with combined spices. Roast, uncovered, in hot oven about 15 minutes or until browned both sides and cooked as desired.
4 Meanwhile, roast corn on heated lightly oiled grill plate (or grill or barbecue) until browned all over. When corn is just cool enough to handle, cut kernels from cobs with a small, sharp knife.
5 Combine corn kernels in medium bowl with remaining ingredients. Serve fish with salsa.

per serving 15g fat; 1832kJ (438 cal); 3.4g saturated fat; 8.7g fibre; 26.1g carbohydrate; low GI

crisp-skinned snapper with stir-fried vegetables and black beans

preparation time 15 minutes
cooking time 10 minutes
serves 4

½ teaspoon sea salt
1 teaspoon coarsely ground black pepper
4 x 200g snapper fillets
1 teaspoon sesame oil
1 large brown onion (200g), cut into thin wedges
1 clove garlic, crushed
1 teaspoon grated fresh ginger
1 tablespoon salted black beans, rinsed, drained
1 medium green pepper (200g), chopped coarsely
1 medium red pepper (200g), chopped coarsely
6 spring onions, sliced thickly
100g mangetout
100g tenderstem broccoli, chopped coarsely
½ cup (125ml) water
¼ cup (60ml) oyster sauce
2 tablespoons lemon juice
500g baby pak choy, chopped coarsely
1 cup (80g) beansprouts

1 Combine salt and pepper in small bowl; rub into skin side of each fillet. Cook fish, skin-side down, on heated lightly oiled grill plate (or grill or barbecue) until browned and crisp; turn, cook until browned and cooked as desired. Cover to keep warm.
2 Heat oil in wok or large frying pan; stir-fry brown onion, garlic and ginger until onion softens. Add beans; stir-fry 1 minute. Add pepper, spring onion, mangetout and broccoli; stir-fry until vegetables are just tender.
3 Stir in the water, sauce and juice; cook, stirring, until mixture thickens slightly. Add pak choy and beansprouts; stir-fry until heated through. Serve fish on vegetables.

per serving 5.3g fat; 1223kJ (292 cal); 1.4g saturated fat; 5.4g fibre; 12.6g carbohydrate; low GI

TIPS Tenderstem broccoli, a cross between broccoli and Chinese kale, is milder and sweeter than normal broccoli. Each long stem is topped by a loose floret that closely resembles broccoli; from floret to stem, broccolini is completely edible.

artichoke risotto

preparation time 10 minutes
cooking time 25 minutes
serves 6

2 teaspoons olive oil
1 medium brown onion (150g), chopped finely
3 cloves garlic, crushed
6 spring onions, sliced thinly
2 cups (400g) gluten-free rice
¾ cup (180ml) dry white wine
1½ cups (375ml) chicken stock
3 cups (750ml) water
400g can artichoke hearts, drained, sliced thinly
½ cup (40g) finely grated parmesan cheese

1 Heat oil in large saucepan; cook brown onion, garlic and half of the spring onion, stirring, until brown onion softens. Add rice, wine, stock and the water; bring to a boil. Reduce heat; simmer, covered, 15 minutes, stirring occasionally.
2 Stir in artichokes, cheese and remaining spring onion; cook, stirring, about 5 minutes or until artichokes are heated through.
TIP While the short-grained arborio is traditionally used in a risotto, we chose to use a longer-grained gluten-free rice here because it has both a lower GI rating and is more amenable to being cooked with the liquids added all at once. Use basmati rice if you can't get gluten-free.

per serving 4.5g fat; 1353kJ (323 cal); 1.2g saturated fat; 1.8g fibre; 37g carbohydrate; medium GI

linguine with lamb, asparagus and gremolata

preparation time 20 minutes
cooking time 15 minutes
serves 6

375g linguine
375g lamb fillets
500g asparagus, trimmed, chopped coarsely
⅓ cup finely grated lemon rind
4 cloves garlic, crushed
1 cup coarsely chopped fresh flat-leaf parsley
½ cup (125ml) lemon juice
8 spring onions, sliced thinly
1 tablespoon olive oil

1 Cook pasta in large saucepan of boiling water until just tender; drain. Place in large bowl; cover to keep warm.
2 Meanwhile, cook lamb on heated lightly oiled grill plate (or grill or barbecue) until browned all over and cooked as desired. Cover; stand 5 minutes, slice thinly.
3 Boil, steam or microwave the asparagus until just tender; drain.
4 Combine remaining ingredients in small bowl; pour over pasta. Add lamb and asparagus; toss gently to combine.
TIP This recipe is good served warm or at room temperature. If not serving immediately, do not toss the ingredients together or the pasta will absorb the dressing.

per serving 6.2g fat; 1382kJ (330 cal); 1g saturated fat; 2.9g fibre; 19.8g carbohydrate; low GI

tofu stir-fry

preparation time 20 minutes (plus standing time)
cooking time 10 minutes
serves 4

400g fresh firm tofu
400g fresh egg noodles
1 tablespoon sesame oil
2 cloves garlic, crushed
2 red thai chillies, deseeded, sliced thinly
1 small red onion (100g), cut into wedges
1 medium red pepper (200g), chopped coarsely
150g green beans, halved
200g chestnut mushrooms, halved
4 spring onions, sliced thinly
2 tablespoons soy sauce
2 tablespoons oyster sauce
1 tablespoon brown sugar

1 Preheat oven to hot. Line oven tray with baking parchment.
2 Press tofu between two chopping boards or trays, place weight on top; elevate boards slightly to allow tofu liquid to drain away. Stand 20 minutes; cut tofu into 2cm cubes. Place tofu on prepared oven tray; cook, uncovered, in hot oven about 25 minutes or until lightly browned.
3 Meanwhile, place noodles in large heatproof bowl, cover with boiling water; stand until just tender, separating noodles carefully with a fork. Drain; cover to keep warm.
4 Heat oil in wok or large frying pan; stir-fry garlic, chilli and red onion until onion softens. Add pepper; stir-fry 2 minutes. Add beans and mushrooms; stir-fry until vegetables are just tender. Add tofu with spring onion, sauces and sugar; stir-fry until sauce thickens slightly. Serve stir-fry tossed with noodles.
TIP Some Asian supermarkets sell tofu already fried and cut into squares; while this will contain more fat than our oven-browned tofu, it also will shorten the preparation time for this dish.

per serving 11.3 g fat; 2474kJ (591 cal); 1.6g saturated fat; 8.3g fibre; 90.1g carbohydrate; low GI

swiss chard, mushroom and pepper frittata

preparation time 15 minutes
cooking time 45 minutes
serves 4

500g swiss chard, trimmed, chopped coarsely
1 tablespoon low-fat dairy-free spread
1 medium brown onion (150g), chopped finely
2 cloves garlic, crushed
1 medium red pepper (200g), chopped finely
2 trimmed sticks celery (150g), chopped finely
100g button mushrooms, sliced thinly
2 large carrots (360g), grated coarsely
¼ cup (40g) polenta
¼ cup coarsely chopped fresh basil
3 eggs, beaten lightly
3 egg whites, beaten lightly
⅓ cup (80ml) skimmed milk

1 Preheat oven to moderate.
2 Line 20cm x 30cm baking tin with baking parchment.
3 Boil, steam or microwave swiss chard; drain on absorbent paper.
4 Melt spread in large deep frying pan; cook onion and garlic, stirring, until onion softens. Add pepper, celery and mushrooms; cook, stirring, until vegetables just soften.
5 Stir swiss chard, carrot, polenta and basil into vegetable mixture. Remove from heat; cool 5 minutes. Add eggs, whites and milk; stir to combine. Spread frittata mixture into prepared tin; bake, uncovered, in moderate oven about 35 minutes or until lightly browned and firm to the touch.
TIP This frittata is just as good eaten at room temperature as it is hot from the oven.

per serving 6.7g fat; 809kJ (193 cal); 1.6g saturated fat; 8.3g fibre; 19.3g carbohydrate; medium GI

roast baby vegetable pizza

preparation time 15 minutes
cooking time 40 minutes
serves 4

3 small courgettes (160g), sliced thinly
4 baby aubergines (240g), sliced thinly
10 cherry tomatoes, halved
1 baby fennel (130g), sliced thinly
100g button mushrooms, sliced thinly
⅔ cup (190g) bottled tomato pasta sauce
¼ cup coarsely chopped fresh basil
4 wholemeal pocket pitta
⅓ cup (40g) coarsely grated low-fat cheddar cheese

1 Preheat oven to hot.
2 Place courgette, aubergine and tomato in lightly oiled shallow medium baking dish; roast, uncovered, 20 minutes.
3 Add fennel, mushrooms and all but 2 tablespoons of the pasta sauce to dish; roast, covered, 10 minutes. Stir basil into vegetable mixture.
4 Divide reserved pasta sauce among bread pieces; top each with equal amounts of the vegetable mixture and cheese. Place on oven tray; cook, uncovered, in hot oven about 10 minutes or until cheese melts and pizzas are heated through.

per serving 2.9g fat; 1016kJ (243 cal); 0.8g saturated fat; 8.1g fibre; 24.2g carbohydrate; high GI

lentil cottage pie

preparation time 10 minutes
cooking time 45 minutes (plus standing time)
serves 4

800g medium new potatoes, quartered
2 tablespoons low-fat dairy-free spread
1 medium brown onion (150g), chopped finely
1 clove garlic, crushed
415g can crushed tomatoes
1 cup (250ml) vegetable stock
1 cup (250ml) water
2 tablespoons tomato paste
⅓ cup (80ml) dry red wine
⅔ cup (130g) red lentils
1 medium carrot (120g), chopped finely
½ cup (60g) frozen peas, thawed
2 tablespoons worcestershire sauce
⅓ cup coarsely chopped fresh flat-leaf parsley

1 Preheat oven to hot.
2 Boil, steam or microwave potato until tender; drain. Mash in large bowl with half of the spread.
3 Melt remaining spread in medium deep frying pan; cook onion and garlic, stirring, until onion softens. Add undrained tomatoes, stock, the water, paste, wine, lentils and carrot; bring to a boil. Reduce heat; simmer, uncovered, 15 minutes, stirring occasionally. Add peas, sauce and parsley; cook, uncovered, 5 minutes.
4 Spoon lentil mixture into shallow 1-litre (4 cup) ovenproof dish. Spread potato mash over the top. Bake, uncovered, in hot oven 20 minutes. Stand pie 10 minutes before serving.
TIP If you're not concerned with keeping the fat content of this dish low, you can stir ½ cup of finely grated parmesan cheese into the potato mash before baking the cottage pie.

per serving 7.2g fat; 1341kJ (320 cal); 1.2g saturated fat; 11.3g fibre; 45.1g carbohydrate; high GI

dhal with egg and aubergine

preparation time 10 minutes
cooking time 1 hour
serves 4

2 cups (400g) red lentils
2 teaspoons vegetable oil
1 medium brown onion (150g), chopped finely
1 clove garlic, crushed
2 teaspoons ground cumin
½ teaspoon cumin seeds
1 tablespoon tomato paste
1 litre (4 cups) water
2 cups (500ml) vegetable stock
1 large tomato (250g), chopped coarsely
3 baby aubergines (180g), chopped coarsely
4 hard-boiled eggs

1 Rinse lentils in large colander under cold water until water runs clear.
2 Heat oil in large heavy-based saucepan; cook onion, garlic, ground cumin, seeds and paste, stirring, 5 minutes. Add lentils with the water and stock; bring to a boil. Reduce heat; simmer, uncovered, about 40 minutes or until dhal mixture thickens slightly, stirring occasionally.
3 Add tomato and aubergine; simmer, uncovered, about 20 minutes or until dhal is thickened and aubergine is tender, stirring occasionally. Add whole eggs; stir gently until eggs are heated through.
TIP Spoon a whole egg into each of four serving bowls then spoon dhal over the egg.

per serving 10.9g fat; 1698kJ (406 cal); 2.6g saturated fat; 16.7g fibre; 44.6g carbohydrate; low GI

singapore noodles

preparation time 10 minutes
cooking time 20 minutes
serves 4

250g rice vermicelli
4 eggs, beaten lightly
2 teaspoons vegetable oil
1 medium brown onion (150g), chopped coarsely
2 cloves garlic, crushed
2 teaspoons grated fresh ginger
150g baby pak choy, chopped coarsely
200g mangetout, halved
1 small red pepper (150g), sliced thickly
2 tablespoons soy sauce
2 tablespoons oyster sauce
2 tablespoons sweet chilli sauce
1 cup loosely packed fresh coriander leaves
3 cups (240g) beansprouts

1 Place noodles in large heatproof bowl, cover with boiling water, stand until just tender; drain. Using scissors, cut noodles into 10cm lengths.
2 Heat lightly oiled wok or large non-stick frying pan; add half of the egg, swirling wok to form thin omelette. Remove omelette from wok; roll into cigar shape, cut into thin slices. Repeat with remaining egg.
3 Heat oil in same wok; stir-fry onion until soft. Add garlic and ginger; cook, stirring, 1 minute. Add pak choy, mangetout, pepper and sauces; cook, stirring, until vegetables are just tender.
4 Add noodles and egg strips with coriander and beansprouts to wok; toss gently to combine.

per serving 9.9g fat; 1545kJ (369 cal); 2.1g saturated fat; 6.8g fibre; 52.5g carbohydrate; medium GI

satay beef and stir-fried vegetables with rice

preparation time 20 minutes
cooking time 20 minutes
serves 4

1 litre (4 cups) water
1 cup (200g) basmati rice
1 teaspoon ground oil
500g lean beef topside, sliced thinly
1 large brown onion (200g), sliced thinly
1 clove garlic, crushed
2 teaspoons grated fresh ginger
2 red thai chillies, deseeded, chopped finely
1 medium red pepper (200g), chopped coarsely
1 medium green pepper (200g), chopped coarsely
100g button mushrooms, halved
225g can bamboo shoots, drained
1 teaspoon curry powder
2 teaspoons cornflour
½ cup (125ml) chicken stock
¼ cup (65g) low-fat smooth peanut butter
2 tablespoons oyster sauce
1 tablespoon unsalted, roasted, coarsely chopped peanuts

1 Bring the water to a boil in large saucepan; stir in rice. Boil, uncovered, about 15 minutes or until rice is just tender. Drain, rinse under hot water; drain rice again, cover to keep warm.
2 Meanwhile, heat oil in wok or large non-stick frying pan; stir-fry beef, in batches, until browned all over.
3 Reheat meat juices in same wok; stir-fry onion and garlic until onion softens. Add ginger, chilli, peppers, mushrooms, bamboo shoots and curry powder; stir-fry until vegetables are just tender.
4 Blend cornflour with stock in small jug; pour into wok, stir to combine with vegetable mixture. Return beef to wok with peanut butter and oyster sauce; bring to a boil, stirring, until sauce boils and thickens slightly and beef is cooked as desired. Stir in peanuts; serve with rice.
TIP You can use sliced lamb fillets or sliced chicken thigh fillets instead of the beef, if you prefer.

per serving 14g fat; 2387kJ (570 cal); 2.3g saturated fat; 4g fibre; 70g carbohydrate; medium GI

desserts and cakes

chocolate ricotta tart

preparation time 15 minutes (plus refrigeration time)
cooking time 35 minutes
serves 8

¼ cup (35g) white self-raising flour
¼ cup (40g) wholemeal self-raising flour
2 tablespoons caster sugar
2 teaspoons cocoa powder
30g low-fat dairy-free spread
2 teaspoons water
1 egg yolk

RICOTTA FILLING
150g low-fat ricotta
1 egg
1 egg yolk
¼ cup (70g) low-fat plain yogurt
¼ cup (55g) caster sugar
2 teaspoons white plain flour
2 tablespoons dark chocolate chips
2 teaspoons coffee-flavoured liqueur

1 Grease 18cm-round loose-based flan tin.
2 Process flours, sugar, sifted cocoa and spread until crumbly; add the water and egg yolk, process until ingredients just cling together. Knead dough gently on lightly floured surface until smooth, cover; refrigerate 30 minutes.
3 Preheat oven to moderately hot.
4 Press dough into prepared tin; cover with baking parchment large enough to extend 5cm over edge, fill with dried beans or rice. Bake, on oven tray, in moderately hot oven 10 minutes; remove beans and paper. Bake further 5 minutes or until pastry is lightly browned; cool.
5 Reduce temperature to moderate. Pour ricotta filling into tin; bake, uncovered, in moderate oven about 20 minutes. Cool; refrigerate until firm.

RICOTTA FILLING
Using electric mixer, beat ricotta, egg, egg yolk, yogurt, sugar and flour in medium bowl until smooth. Stir in chocolate chips and liqueur.

per serving 6.5g fat; 706kJ (169 cal); 2.9g saturated fat; 1.2g fibre; 21g carbohydrate; medium GI

citrus rice pudding

preparation time 15 minutes (plus standing time)
cooking time 1 hour 10 minutes
serves 8

2 cups (500ml) skimmed milk
1 vanilla pod, halved lengthways
1 teaspoon finely grated lemon rind
1 teaspoon finely grated lime rind
2 teaspoons finely grated orange rind
2 eggs
1 egg white
½ cup (110g) caster sugar
1½ cups (225g) cooked gluten-free rice
½ cup (125ml) low-fat cream

1 Preheat oven to moderately low. Grease shallow oval 1.5-litre (6 cup) ovenproof dish.
2 Combine milk, vanilla pod and rinds in medium saucepan; bring to a boil. Remove from heat; stand, covered, 5 minutes.
3 Meanwhile, whisk eggs, egg white and sugar in medium bowl. Gradually whisk hot milk mixture into egg mixture; discard vanilla pod.
4 Spread rice into prepared dish; pour egg mixture carefully over rice. Place dish in large baking dish; add enough boiling water to baking dish to come halfway up side of pudding dish.
5 Bake, uncovered, in moderately low oven about 1 hour or until set. Serve warm with cream.
TIP You need to cook about ½ cup of rice for this recipe. Use basmati rice if you can't get hold of gluten-free.

per serving 4.8g fat; 1094kJ (261 cal); 1.7g saturated fat; 0.2g fibre; 31.7g carbohydrate; medium GI

apple bread pudding

preparation time 20 minutes
cooking time 1 hour 10 minutes (plus standing time)
serves 6

2 medium apples (300g)
2 tablespoons brown sugar
1 tablespoon water
2½ cups (625ml) skimmed milk
1 vanilla pod, halved lengthways
4 slices thick fruit bread
3 eggs
½ teaspoon ground cinnamon
¼ teaspoon ground nutmeg

1 Peel and core apples; cut into 3mm slices. Dissolve brown sugar in the water in medium frying pan over low heat, add apples; simmer, uncovered, about 5 minutes or until tender, stirring occasionally.
2 Preheat oven to moderately low. Grease deep 1.5-litre (6 cup) ovenproof dish.
3 Combine milk and vanilla pod in medium saucepan; bring to a boil. Remove from heat; stand, covered, 5 minutes. Discard vanilla pod.
4 Meanwhile, cut bread slices into quarters. Arrange bread and apple in alternate layers in prepared dish.
5 Whisk eggs, cinnamon and nutmeg in medium bowl. Gradually whisk hot milk mixture into egg mixture. Pour egg mixture carefully over bread and apple. Place dish in large baking dish; add enough boiling water to baking dish to come halfway up side of pudding dish.
6 Bake, uncovered, in moderately low oven about 1 hour or until set. Serve with low-fat ice-cream or cream, if desired.

per serving 3.6g fat; 698kJ (167 cal); 1.1g saturated fat; 1.7g fibre; 25.5g carbohydrate; low GI

florentines with berry ice-cream

preparation time 10 minutes
cooking time 10 minutes
serves 8

¼ cup (30g) toasted muesli
¼ cup (15g) bran flakes
¼ cup (40g) sultanas, chopped coarsely
2 tablespoons finely chopped dried apricots
1 tablespoon finely chopped glacé cherries
1½ tablespoons flaked almonds, toasted
¼ cup (60ml) light condensed milk
1 tablespoon golden syrup
400g low-fat berry ice-cream

1 Preheat oven to moderate. Grease two oven trays; line each with baking parchment.
2 Combine all ingredients except the ice-cream in medium bowl.
3 Drop tablespoons of the mixture onto oven trays about 8cm apart, spread into rounds.
4 Bake in moderate oven about 10 minutes or until florentines are lightly browned; cool on trays.
5 Serve 1½ florentines with 2 scoops of ice-cream.

per serving 3.4g fat; 599kJ (143 cal); 1.4g saturated fat; 0.7g fibre; 25.2g carbohydrate; medium GI

pears poached in cranberry syrup

pears poached in cranberry syrup
preparation time 5 minutes (plus standing time)
cooking time 45 minutes
serves 4

3 cups (750ml) cranberry juice
⅔ cup (160ml) dry white wine
2 cardamom pods, bruised
½ vanilla pod, halved lengthways
4 medium-size firm pears (920g)

1 Combine juice, wine, cardamom and vanilla pod in large saucepan.
2 Add peeled pears to pan; bring to a boil. Reduce heat; simmer, covered, about 25 minutes or until tender. Cool pears in syrup.
3 Remove pears from syrup; strain syrup into medium heatproof bowl. Return 2 cups of the strained syrup to same pan (discard remaining syrup); bring to a boil. Boil, uncovered, about 15 minutes or until syrup is reduced by half. Serve pears, hot or cold, with syrup.
TIPS Beurre bosc, williams or packham pears are all suitable for this recipe. Pears can be poached a day ahead; reduce the syrup just before serving.

per serving 0.2g fat; 1178kJ (281 cal); 0g saturated fat; 3.5g fibre; 26.5g carbohydrate; low GI

pink grapefruit granita with hazelnut wafers

preparation time 20 minutes (plus freezing time)
cooking time 10 minutes
serves 8

1 cup (250ml) water
1 cup (220g) sugar
1 cup (250ml) fresh pink grapefruit juice
¼ cup (60ml) lemon juice
2 egg whites

HAZELNUT WAFERS
1 egg white
¼ cup (55g) caster sugar
2 tablespoons ground hazelnuts
20g low-fat dairy-free spread, melted

1 Stir the water and sugar in small saucepan over heat, without boiling, until sugar dissolves. Bring to a boil; boil 5 minutes without stirring. Remove from heat; stir in juices, cool.
2 Using electric mixer, beat egg whites in small bowl until soft peaks form. Fold grapefruit syrup into egg white mixture; pour into 10cm x 24cm loaf tin. Cover; freeze 3 hours or overnight.
3 Blend or process granita until pale and creamy. Return to loaf tin, cover; freeze 3 hours or overnight. Serve granita with hazelnut wafers.

HAZELNUT WAFERS
Preheat oven to moderate. Grease two oven trays; line each with baking parchment. Using electric mixer, beat egg white in small bowl until soft peaks form; gradually add sugar, beating until sugar dissolves between additions. Add ground hazelnuts and spread; stir until combined. Trace 16 x 7cm circles, 2cm apart, on lined trays. Spread a teaspoon of mixture in each circle. Bake in moderate oven about 5 minutes or until lightly browned. Cool wafers on trays before carefully peeling away parchment.
TIP You will need two large pink grapefruit for this recipe.

per serving 2.3g fat; 713kJ (170 cal); 0.2g saturated fat; 0.2g fibre; 36.7g carbohydrate; medium GI

apricot strudel

preparation time 20 minutes
cooking time 20 minutes
serves 6

825g can apricot slices in natural syrup, drained
2 tablespoons brown sugar
1 teaspoon ground cinnamon
¾ cup (120g) sultanas
¼ cup (35g) roasted hazelnuts, chopped finely
6 sheets filo pastry
1 tablespoon skimmed milk
1 tablespoon icing sugar

1 Preheat oven to moderately hot. Grease oven tray.
2 Combine apricots, sugar, cinnamon, sultanas and nuts in medium bowl.
3 Stack filo sheets, brushing each lightly with milk as you layer. Spread apricot filling over filo, leaving 5cm space at edge of both short sides and 2cm at edge of one long side. Fold short sides over; starting from filled long-side edge, roll strudel to enclose filling. Place, seam-side down, on prepared tray.
4 Brush strudel with remaining milk. Bake, uncovered, in moderately hot oven about 25 minutes or until lightly browned. Dust strudel with icing sugar before serving, warm or cold, with ice-cream, if desired.

per serving 2.6g fat; 585kJ (143 cal); 0.2g saturated fat; 2g fibre; 20.6g carbohydrate; medium GI

vanilla ice-cream with espresso sauce

preparation time 10 minutes (plus freezing time)
cooking time 15 minutes (plus standing time)
serves 4

1 vanilla pod
1 cup (250ml) light evaporated milk
⅓ cup (80ml) light cream
2 egg yolks
½ cup (110g) caster sugar
½ cup (125ml) boiling water
1 tablespoon ground espresso coffee beans

1 Split vanilla pod lengthways; scrape seeds into small saucepan. Add vanilla pod, evaporated milk and cream; bring to a boil. Remove pan from heat, cover; stand 20 minutes. Discard vanilla pod.
2 Meanwhile, using electric mixer, beat egg yolks and sugar in small bowl until thick and creamy; gradually stir in vanilla mixture.
3 Return mixture to same pan; cook, stirring, over low heat, about 15 minutes or until mixture thickens slightly (do not allow to boil).
4 Strain ice-cream mixture into 20cm x 30cm baking tin, cover surface with foil; cool to room temperature. Freeze until almost set.
5 Place ice-cream in large bowl; chop coarsely. Using electric mixer, beat until smooth. Pour mixture into 14cm x 21cm loaf tin, cover; freeze until ice-cream is firm.
6 Just before serving, combine the water and coffee in coffee plunger; stand 2 minutes before plunging. Cool

tiramisu

preparation time 20 minutes (plus refrigeration time)
cooking time 25 minutes
serves 12

3 eggs
½ cup (110g) caster sugar
¼ cup (40g) wholemeal self-raising flour
¼ cup (35g) white self-raising flour
¼ cup (35g) cornflour
1 teaspoon gelatine
1 tablespoon cold water
1½ cups (300g) low-fat ricotta cheese
¼ cup (60ml) skimmed milk
¼ cup (55g) caster sugar, extra
2 tablespoons instant coffee powder
2 tablespoons boiling water
⅓ cup (80ml) skimmed milk, extra
½ cup (125ml) coffee-flavoured liqueur
10g dark chocolate, grated finely

1 Preheat oven to moderate. Grease and line base of 22cm springform tin.
2 Using electric mixer, beat eggs in small bowl until thick and creamy. Gradually add sugar, beating until sugar dissolves. Fold triple-sifted flours into egg mixture until just combined. Spread into prepared tin.
3 Bake, uncovered, in moderate oven about 25 minutes. Turn onto wire rack to cool.
4 Meanwhile, sprinkle gelatine over the cold water in small heatproof jug; place jug in small pan of simmering water, stir until gelatine dissolves. Cool, 5 minutes.
5 Blend or process ricotta, milk and extra sugar until smooth. With motor operating, add gelatine mixture; process until combined. Dissolve coffee in the boiling water in small bowl; add extra milk and liqueur.
6 Cut cake in half horizontally. Return one cake half to same springform tin; brush half of the coffee mixture over cake; top with half of the ricotta mixture. Repeat with remaining cake half, coffee mixture and ricotta mixture.
7 Refrigerate tiramisu, covered, for at least 3 hours. Sprinkle top with grated chocolate just before serving.

per serving 4.1g fat; 791kJ (189 cal); 2g saturated fat; 0.9g fibre; 28g carbohydrate; medium GI

berry mousse

preparation time 10 minutes (plus refrigeration time)
serves 4

2 teaspoons gelatine
2 tablespoons water
2 egg whites
⅓ cup (75g) caster sugar
2 x 200g cartons low-fat berry-flavoured yogurt
150g fresh mixed berries

1 Sprinkle gelatine over the water in small heatproof jug; place jug in small pan of simmering water, stir until gelatine dissolves, cool.
2 Meanwhile, using electric mixer, beat egg whites in small bowl until soft peaks form. Gradually add sugar, beating until sugar dissolves.
3 Place yogurt in medium bowl; stir in gelatine mixture, fold in egg white mixture. Spoon mousse mixture into serving bowl, cover; refrigerate about 2 hours or until set. Top mousse with berries to serve.

per serving 0.2g fat; 708kJ (169 cal); 0.1g saturated fat; 0.9g fibre; 32.8g carbohydrate; low GI

yogurt and mango jelly

preparation time 5 minutes (plus refrigeration time)
serves 6

85g packet orange jelly crystals
1 cup (250ml) boiling water
2 x 200g cartons low-fat mango yogurt
1 medium mango (430g), chopped finely
1 medium banana (200g), sliced thinly
1 medium kiwi fruit (85g), halved, sliced thinly
2 tablespoons passionfruit pulp

1 Stir jelly crystals with the water in small heatproof bowl until dissolved; refrigerate about 20 minutes or until cold (do not allow to set).
2 Add yogurt and mango to jelly; stir to combine. Divide jelly mixture among six 1-cup (250ml) serving glasses. Cover; refrigerate about 2 hours or until set. Just before serving, top each jelly with equal amounts of banana, kiwi fruit and passionfruit.
TIPS We used golden kiwi fruit in this recipe. You need about 2 passionfruit for this recipe.

per serving 1g fat; 720kJ (172 cal); 0.5g saturated fat; 2.6g fibre; 36.3g carbohydrate; low GI

raspberry yogurt cake

preparation time 30 minutes
cooking time 1 hour 5 minutes
serves 12

½ cup (125g) low-fat dairy-free spread
¾ cup (165g) firmly packed brown sugar
2 eggs
1¼ cups (200g) wholemeal self-raising flour
½ cup (140g) low-fat plain yogurt
100g frozen raspberries

CREAM-CHEESE FROSTING
80g light cream cheese, softened
⅓ cup (55g) icing sugar
1 teaspoon lemon juice

1 Preheat oven to moderate. Grease 14cm x 21cm loaf tin; line base and two long sides with baking parchment, extending paper 5cm above edges of tin.
2 Using electric mixer, beat spread and sugar in medium bowl until light and fluffy. Add eggs, one at a time, beating until just combined.
3 Transfer mixture to medium bowl; stir in flour, yogurt and raspberries. Spread mixture into prepared tin.
4 Bake, uncovered, in moderate oven about 1 hour 5 minutes. Stand 10 minutes, turn onto wire rack; turn top-side up to cool. Place cake on serving plate; using spatula, spread cake top with cream-cheese frosting.

CREAM-CHEESE FROSTING
Whisk cheese, sugar and lemon juice in small bowl until smooth.

per serving 1.5g fat; 572kJ (137 cal); 0.8g saturated fat; 2.3g fibre; 28g carbohydrate; medium GI

chocolate brownie

preparation time 15 minutes
cooking time 25 minutes
makes 16

2 eggs
⅓ cup (75g) firmly packed brown sugar
2 teaspoons instant coffee powder
2 tablespoons cocoa powder
1 tablespoon water
1 tablespoon olive oil
40g low-fat dairy-free spread, melted
¼ cup (40g) wholemeal self-raising flour
¼ cup (45g) dark chocolate chips
1 teaspoon cocoa powder, extra
2 teaspoons icing sugar

1 Preheat oven to moderate. Grease and line deep 19cm-square baking tin.
2 Using electric mixer, beat eggs and sugar in small bowl until thick and creamy. Transfer to medium bowl.
3 Meanwhile, blend coffee and cocoa with the water and oil in small bowl until smooth. Stir in spread. Fold cocoa mixture into egg mixture; fold in flour and chocolate chips. Pour mixture into prepared pan.
4 Bake, uncovered, in moderate oven for about 25 minutes or until brownie is firm to the touch. Stand 30 minutes; turn onto wire rack. Serve brownie dusted with sifted combined extra cocoa and icing sugar, and low-fat ice-cream, if desired.

per brownie 3.8g fat; 303kJ (73 cal); 0.6g saturated fat; 0.2g fibre; 4.7g carbohydrate; medium GI

fig-topped cheesecake

preparation time 25 minutes (plus refrigeration time)
serves 16

11 plain sweet biscuits (135g)
2 teaspoons gelatine
2 tablespoons water
200g low-fat yogurt
250g light cream cheese, softened
¼ cup (90g) honey
1 teaspoon ground cardamom
2 fresh figs (120g), cut into wedges

1 Grease deep 19cm-square cake tin; line base and sides with baking parchment, extending 5cm above two opposing sides of tin.
2 Place biscuits in prepared tin; trim to cover base in a single layer.
3 Sprinkle gelatine over the water in small heatproof jug; place jug in small pan of simmering water, stir until gelatine dissolves. Cool 5 minutes.
4 Using electric mixer, beat yogurt and cream cheese in small bowl until smooth. Stir in honey and cardamom then gelatine mixture; pour into prepared tin. Cover; refrigerate about 4 hours or until set. Serve cheesecake topped with figs.
TIP 'Nice' biscuits make a perfect base for this yummy cheesecake.

per serving 3.6g fat; 387kJ (92 cal); 1.3g saturated fat; 0.2g fibre; 6.6g carbohydrate; medium GI

moist orange cake

preparation time 15 minutes
cooking time 20 minutes (plus standing time)
serves 12

4 large oranges (1.2kg)
60g low-fat dairy-free spread
1 cup (220g) caster sugar
2 eggs
⅓ cup (40g) ground almonds
1 cup (160g) wholemeal self-raising flour
2 tablespoons skimmed soy milk

1 Preheat oven to moderately low. Grease and line shallow 23cm-round cake tin.

2 Finely grate ½ teaspoon of rind from 1 orange; slice 1 tablespoon of thin strips of rind from same orange. Reserve rinds. Squeeze the peeled orange; reserve ⅔ cup (160ml) juice. Peel remaining 3 oranges; separate into segments. Reserve segments.

3 Using electric mixer, beat spread, ⅓ cup of the sugar and the finely grated rind in small bowl until pale and creamy. Add eggs; beat until combined. Add ground almonds, flour, 1 tablespoon of the orange juice and milk; stir to combine. Spread batter into prepared tin. Bake, uncovered, in moderately low oven about 20 minutes.

4 Meanwhile, combine remaining juice and remaining sugar in small saucepan over heat, without boiling, until sugar dissolves; bring to a boil. Add reserved rind strips, reduce heat; simmer, uncovered, about 3 minutes or until syrup thickens slightly.

5 Remove cake from oven. Stand 5 minutes; turn onto wire rack. Using skewer, pierce cake several times; brush with ¼ cup of the hot syrup. Serve cake sliced, with reserved orange segments and remaining syrup.

per serving 5.3g fat; 755kJ (180 cal); 0.8g saturated fat; 2.5g fibre; 30.7g carbohydrate; medium GI

pear oatmeal cake

preparation time 15 minutes (plus standing time)
cooking time 1 hour
serves 16

2 x 425g cans pear halves in syrup
1 cup (90g) rolled oats
½ cup (125g) low-fat dairy-free spread
½ teaspoon vanilla essence
¾ cup (150g) firmly packed brown sugar
2 eggs
¾ cup (110g) white self-raising flour
¾ cup (120g) wholemeal self-raising flour
½ teaspoon bicarbonate of soda
2 teaspoons ground ginger

1 Preheat oven to moderately hot. Grease and line sides of deep 23cm-square cake tin.
2 Drain pears over small saucepan. Heat syrup with oats, remove from heat; stand 20 minutes.
3 Meanwhile, using electric mixer, beat spread, vanilla and sugar in small bowl until combined. Beat in eggs, one at a time, until combined.
4 Add oat mixture and combined sifted remaining ingredients; stir until well combined. Pour mixture into prepared tin; place pears on top, cut-side down.
5 Bake, uncovered, in moderately hot oven about 55 minutes. Serve warm.

per serving 4.5g fat; 720kJ (170 cal); 0.8g saturated fat; 2.6g fibre; 30g carbohydrate; medium GI

wholemeal date loaf

preparation time 20 minutes
cooking time 1 hour
serves 14

1 cup (170g) pitted dates, halved
2 tablespoons boiling water
½ teaspoon bicarbonate of soda
60g low-fat dairy-free spread
2 teaspoons finely grated lemon rind
¾ cup (150g) firmly packed brown sugar
200g low-fat cottage cheese
2 eggs
2 cups (320g) wholemeal self-raising flour
2 tablespoons wheat germ

1 Preheat oven to moderately low. Grease 14cm x 21cm loaf tin; line base and two long sides with baking parchment, extending paper 5cm above edges of tin.
2 Combine dates, the water and bicarbonate of soda in small bowl, cover; stand 5 minutes.
3 Using electric mixer, beat spread, rind and sugar in small bowl until light and fluffy. Add cheese; beat until smooth. Add eggs, one at a time; beat until combined.
4 Stir in flour, wheat germ and date mixture; pour into prepared pan.
5 Bake, uncovered, in moderately low oven about 1 hour. Stand 10 minutes; turn onto wire rack to cool.

per serving 3.2g fat; 779kJ (186 cal); 0.5g saturated fat; 2.9g fibre; 23.7g carbohydrate; high GI

plum and cinnamon cake

preparation time 15 minutes
cooking time 35 minutes
serves 12

½ cup (125g) low-fat dairy-free spread
1 teaspoon vanilla essence
½ cup (100g) firmly packed brown sugar
3 eggs, separated
½ cup (75g) white self-raising flour
½ cup (80g) wholemeal self-raising flour
1 teaspoon ground cinnamon
4 whole canned plums in syrup, drained, halved, pitted

1 Preheat oven to moderate. Grease 20cm ring cake tin; line base and sides with baking parchment.
2 Using electric mixer, beat spread, essence, sugar and egg yolks in small bowl until light and fluffy. Transfer mixture to medium bowl; stir in flours and cinnamon.
3 Using electric mixer, beat egg whites in small bowl until soft peaks form; gently fold whites into cake batter.
4 Spread batter into prepared tin; place plums on top, cut-side down. Bake, uncovered, in moderate oven about 30 minutes. Stand 10 minutes; turn onto wire rack, turn top-side up to cool. Serve dusted with icing sugar, if desired.

TIP You'll probably have to open an 810g can of whole plums in syrup to get the required amount for this recipe. You can serve the remaining plums alongside this cake, or you can freeze them (in the syrup) until you wish to use them for another recipe.

per serving 6.8g fat; 832kJ (198 cal); 2.5g saturated fat; 1.2g fibre; 18.6g carbohydrate; medium GI

strawberry and rhubarb muffins

preparation time 15 minutes
cooking time 20 minutes
makes 12

125g strawberries, sliced thinly
3 cups (450g) wholemeal self-raising flour
½ cup (100g) firmly packed brown sugar
1 teaspoon ground cinnamon
1 teaspoon vanilla essence
60g low-fat dairy-free spread, melted
¾ cup (180ml) skimmed soy milk
2 eggs, beaten lightly
2 cups (250g) finely chopped rhubarb
¼ cup (60g) apple sauce

1 Preheat oven to moderately hot. Grease 12-hole (⅓ cup/80ml) muffin tray. Reserve 12 slices of strawberry.
2 Combine flour, sugar and cinnamon in large bowl. Add essence, spread, milk and eggs; mix to combine then gently stir in remaining strawberries, rhubarb and apple sauce.
3 Divide mixture among holes of prepared tray; top each with a reserved strawberry slice. Bake in moderately hot oven about 20 minutes. Serve warm or at room temperature.
TIP You need about 4 large trimmed stems of rhubarb for this recipe.

per muffin 4.3g fat; 844kJ (202 cal); 0.8g saturated fat; 5.2g fibre; 34.2g carbohydrate; medium GI

apricot upside-down cakes

preparation time 20 minutes
cooking time 20 minutes
makes 12 cakes

1 tablespoon brown sugar
12 canned apricot halves in syrup, drained
2 eggs
¾ cup (150g) firmly packed brown sugar, extra
¾ cup (90g) ground almonds
1 teaspoon vanilla essence
⅓ cup (50g) wholemeal self-raising flour
½ cup (125ml) skimmed milk
¼ cup (80g) light apricot conserve, heated

1 Preheat oven to moderate. Grease 12-hole (⅓ cup/80ml) muffin tray.
2 Sprinkle sugar equally into holes of prepared tray; add 1 apricot half, cut-side down, to each hole.
3 Using electric mixer, beat eggs and extra sugar in medium bowl until light and fluffy. Stir in ground almonds, essence, flour and milk. Divide mixture among holes of prepared tray.
4 Bake in moderate oven about 20 minutes. Stand 5 minutes; turn onto wire rack, brush apricot conserve over hot cakes. Serve cakes warm or at room temperature.
TIP You'll probably have to open a 415g can of apricot halves to get the required amount for this recipe. Serve the remaining apricot halves with the cakes.

per cake 5.2g fat; 554kJ (132 cal); 0.6g saturated fat; 1.4g fibre; 18.2g carbohydrate; medium GI

low fat food

Diet is not synonymous with deprivation, despite what a lot of self-help pundits would have you believe. And reducing your fat intake doesn't mean you have to eliminate fats altogether. It's easy to eat well without taking a degree in nutrition; without leaving out the "good stuff" and replacing it with packaged, chemical or artificial substitutes; without spending hours making special dietary dishes no one else in the family will touch; and ... without going without.

real cooking for a real life

Every year 'new' nutritional advice changes and contradicts most of the trends and beliefs that have gone before. But there does seem to be one given in the midst of it all, and it's quite simple: eating reasonably sized, well-balanced meals and taking moderate exercise regularly will help keep you happy, healthy and of a constant weight that's right for your age, build and gender.

We all know what happens when we go on a radical diet and the weight just falls away: the minute we go off the diet and back to our normal eating habits, the weight reappears – faster, greater – and we're back on the same relentless treadmill again.

In this section we aim to put a halt to the feast or famine routine that traps so many of us. Filled with delicious meal ideas that don't baulk at the inclusion of fats or carbs, and recipes providing alternative suggestions to the 'bad' content of some of our traditional dishes, this isn't about dieting. There are no lists of what you can or cannot eat, no daily consumption chart, no incontrovertible rules. What you will find, however, is real cooking for real life.

Exercise regularly; a couch-potato lifestyle slows your basic metabolism . . .

GET THE 'REGULAR' HABIT

One key word to remember in the search for maintaining your healthy weight is 'regular'. Eat regular meals; don't graze or snack in between. Exercise regularly; a couch-potato lifestyle slows your basic metabolism so you'll need to impose more stringent restrictions on your dietary intake. Your body's energy consumption increases with exercise so, by sticking to a sensible healthy eating plan, you will gradually lose weight – and keep it off – from your early 20s through and beyond your menopausal years.

The breakfast, brunch, soup, dessert and treat recipes in this section have been developed to contain around 7g of fat per serving; packed lunches are based on around 15g of fat per serving, while main meal recipes can contain up to 20g of fat per serving. This means you can mix and match one selection from each chapter, keeping in mind your daily fat intake should be a maximum of 56g in order to maintain weight.

Consuming more fat per day can lead to an increase in weight, while reducing the amount to about 40g per day, when coupled with exercise, will see the beginning of moderate weight loss.

COOKING THE LOW-FAT WAY
- Always measure the amount of oil you add to a pan, rather than simply adding a slurp by guesswork.
- Stir-fry in a wok or non-stick pan rather than shallow-fry.
- Heat your pan or grill before adding oil – it will spread further, so you will need to use less.
- Add the same amount of stock, water, juice, flavoured vinegar or wine to pan as an alternative to oil or butter.
- Roast meat on a rack in a baking dish. This allows excess fat to drain away from the meat.
- When slow cooking or stewing, trim all fat from meat and poultry before cooking.

DON'T EVEN THINK ABOUT DEEP-FRYING!
Try, instead, to roast 'chips' on a baking-parchment-lined oven tray, spraying them with a light coating of olive oil.

- Prepare casseroles and soups a day ahead and refrigerate so that any fat solidifies on the surface. Skim off all fat before reheating.
- Thicken sauces with pureed vegetables – keep small amounts frozen for the purpose.

LOW-FAT ALTERNATIVES

Don't completely deprive yourself – just replace high-fat foods with an appropriate low-fat alternative.

- Instead of ice-cream or cream, try whipped chilled evaporated milk (serve immediately) or whipped low-fat ricotta cheese, sweetened with icing sugar or powdered sweetner.
- Use buttermilk or low-fat or no-fat yogurt in place of soured cream and full-fat yogurt.
- Use filo pastry as an alternative to shortcrust or puff pastry. Coat filo sheets lightly with cooking-oil spray, skimmed milk or, better yet, water between layers.
- Instead of oil, use the same amount of stock or water. For salad dressings, use an oil-free variety.
- Make your own reduced-fat version of coconut cream by soaking desiccated coconut in low-fat milk; stand for 30 minutes, then strain over a bowl and discard coconut. You can also add a few drops of coconut essence to evaporated low-fat skimmed milk.
- Substitute low-fat margarine or light cream cheese for butter and margarine.
- Always choose a low-fat variety of commercial mayonnaise.
- When selecting cheese, choose low-fat cheddar, mozzarella and ricotta varieties, and remember that a small amount of parmesan cheese (although full-fat) actually gives twice as much flavour as many other cheeses, so you can use less.

SOME VITAL THINGS TO REMEMBER

- Try not to eat takeaway food, and avoid buying commercial cakes and biscuits, which are among the worst sources of the combination of refined sugar and saturated fats.
- Whenever possible, stir-fry in a wok instead of shallow-frying. Heat the wok first before giving the sides a light spray of rapeseed oil.
- Try to only ever use olive oil or rapeseed oil for cooking, and use it sparingly.
- Stock, water or juice can be used instead of oil or butter to soften some ingredients in soups, sauces and casseroles.
- Soups, sauces and casseroles can be thickened with pureed vegetables rather than flour or egg.
- Make soups, sauces and casseroles a day ahead, refrigerate them overnight, then skim away the fat that solidifies on the surface before reheating.
- Eat smaller portions to help prevent your body from storing excess kilojoules.
- Increase your consumption of fish, including canned fish.
- Discard the skin from all poultry.
- Use low-fat or light dairy products.
- Keep only good foods in the house: you won't brave the elements just to go out to buy a tub of chocolate ice-cream.
- Keep track of what you eat in a single day by writing everything down in a small notepad that you keep with you.
- Drink plenty of natural water and make sure you get enough sleep.
- Don't be impatient: one week's worth of exercise will not turn you into Elle Macpherson. Nothing happens overnight.

Focus on fibre: eat lots of whole grains, fruit, vegetables and proteins.

juices and drinks

lemongrass and ginger iced tea

preparation time 10 minutes
makes 1 litre (4 cups)

6 lemongrass and ginger teabags
1 litre (4 cups) boiling water
2 tablespoons grated palm sugar
10cm stick fresh lemongrass (20g), chopped finely
½ small orange (90g), sliced thinly
½ lemon, sliced thinly
¼ cup firmly packed fresh mint leaves, torn
1 cup ice cubes

1 Place teabags and the water in large heatproof jug; stand
5 minutes.
2 Discard teabags. Add sugar, lemongrass, orange and lemon
to jug; stir to combine. Refrigerate, covered, until cold.
3 Stir mint into cold tea; serve immediately over ice.

per 250ml 0.1g fat (0g saturated); 159kJ (38 cal);
8.5g carbohydrate

mango frappé

preparation time 10 minutes
makes 3 cups (750ml)

2 medium mangoes (860g)
3 cups ice cubes
1 tablespoon sugar

1 Halve mangoes, peel, then discard stones. Blend
or process mango flesh with ice cubes and sugar until
thick and smooth.
2 Pour into serving glasses; stand at room temperature
for 5 minutes before serving.

per 250ml 0.4g fat (0g saturated); 569kJ (136 cal);
31.3g carbohydrate

minted tomato, rhubarb and lime frappé

preparation time 5 minutes
makes 1.25 litres (5 cups)

4 cups chopped rhubarb (440g)
¼ cup (55g) sugar
¼ cup (60ml) water
4 medium tomatoes (760g), peeled, deseeded,
chopped
2½ tablespoons lime juice
3 cups ice cubes
2 tablespoons chopped fresh mint

1 Combine rhubarb, sugar and the water in medium
saucepan; simmer, covered, about 10 minutes or until
rhubarb is tender. Cool.
2 Blend or process rhubarb mixture with remaining
ingredients until smooth; serve immediately.

per 250ml 0.4g fat (0g saturated); 334kJ
(80 cal); 15.4g carbohydrate

lemon iced tea

preparation time 5 minutes
makes 1.5 litres (6 cups)

3 teabags
3 lemon soother or lemon zinger teabags
1.5 litres (6 cups) boiling water
⅓ cup (80g) caster sugar
2 strips of lemon rind
1 cup ice cubes

1 Combine teabags, the water, sugar and rind in large heatproof jug, stir until sugar is dissolved; cool to room temperature, strain mixture.
2 Refrigerate until cold. Serve with ice cubes.

per 250ml 0g fat (0g saturated); 217kJ (52 cal);
13.4g carbohydrate

moroccan mint tea

preparation time 5 minutes
makes 1 litre (4 cups)

1 litre (4 cups) hot water
3 teabags
1 cup loosely packed fresh mint leaves
2 tablespoons caster sugar
½ cup loosely packed fresh mint leaves, extra
1 cup ice cubes

1 Combine the water, teabags, mint and sugar in medium heatproof jug, stand 10 minutes; discard teabags. Cover; refrigerate until cool.
2 Strain tea mixture; discard leaves. Add extra mint and ice cubes; serve immediately.

per 250ml 0.2g fat (0g saturated); 176kJ (42 cal);
9.8g carbohydrate

mixed berry smoothie

preparation time 5 minutes
makes 1 litre (4 cups)

250ml frozen low-fat strawberry yogurt, softened slightly
1⅓ cups (200g) frozen mixed berries
3 cups (750ml) skimmed milk

1 Blend ingredients, in batches, until smooth.
2 Serve immediately.

per 250ml 3.6g fat (2.3g saturated); 803kJ (192 cal); 27.9g carbohydrate

banana passionfruit soy smoothie

preparation time 10 minutes
makes 1 litre (4 cups)

½ cup (125ml) passionfruit pulp
2 cups (500ml) soy milk
2 medium ripe bananas (400g), chopped coarsely

1 Strain passionfruit pulp through sieve into small bowl; reserve liquid and seeds.
2 Blend passionfruit liquid, milk and banana, in batches, until smooth.
3 Pour smoothie into large jug; stir in reserved seeds.
TIP You need about six passionfruit for this recipe.

per 250ml 4.7g fat (0.5g saturated); 656kJ (157 cal); 22.5g carbohydrate

banana smoothie

preparation time 5 minutes
makes 1 litre (4 cups)

2 cups (500ml) skimmed milk
2 medium bananas (400g), chopped coarsely
½ cup (140g) low-fat yogurt
1 tablespoon honey
1 tablespoon wheat germ
¼ teaspoon ground cinnamon

1 Blend ingredients until smooth.

per 250ml 0.9g fat (0.5g saturated); 698kJ (167 cal);
30.5g carbohydrate

raspberry cranberry crush

preparation time 5 minutes
makes 1 litre (4 cups)

1 cup (250ml) raspberry sorbet
2 cups (500ml) cranberry juice
1 cup (150g) frozen raspberries
2 tablespoons lemon juice

1 Blend or process ingredients until smooth; serve immediately.
TIP Add a little icing sugar or powdered sweetener if you prefer this drink sweeter.

per 250ml 0.2g fat (0g saturated); 543kJ (130 cal);
31.1g carbohydrate

breakfast and brunch

poached eggs on sourdough bread

preparation time 5 minutes
cooking time 15 minutes
serves 4

4 eggs
8 slices prosciutto (120g)
50g baby spinach leaves
½ loaf sourdough bread (335g)

1 Preheat grill.
2 Half-fill large shallow frying pan with water; bring to a boil. Break eggs into cup, one at a time, then slide into pan. When all eggs are in pan, allow water to return to a boil. Cover pan, turn off heat; stand about 4 minutes or until a light film sets over egg yolks. Remove eggs, one at a time, using slotted spoon; place spoon on absorbent-paper-lined saucer briefly to blot up any liquid.
3 Meanwhile, cook prosciutto, in single layer, under preheated grill.
4 Boil, steam or microwave spinach until just wilted; drain. Using hand, squeeze excess water from spinach.
5 Meanwhile, trim end from bread; cut into four slices. Toast bread both sides; divide among serving plates. Top each with 1 slice prosciutto, a quarter of the spinach and an egg, then top with second slice prosciutto.

per serving 9.2g total fat (2.6g saturated fat); 1313kJ (314 cal); 38g carbohydrate; 19.6g protein; 4.2g fibre

peach bircher muesli

preparation time 25 minutes (plus refrigeration time)
serves 4

2 cups (220g) natural muesli
1⅓ cups (330ml) apple juice
¾ cup (200g) low-fat country-style yogurt
1¼ cups (185g) dried peaches, chopped coarsely
2 tablespoons honey
¾ cup (180ml) skimmed milk
1 medium pear (230g), peeled, grated
1 large peach (220g), cut into wedges
¼ cup (15g) toasted shredded coconut

1 Combine muesli, juice, yogurt, dried peach, honey and milk in large bowl. Cover; refrigerate overnight.
2 Stir pear into muesli mixture; serve topped with peach wedges and sprinkled with coconut.

per serving 8.6g total fat (4.2g saturated fat); 2002kJ (479 cal); 88.1g carbohydrate; 13g protein; 12.5g fibre

rice porridge with dried fruit compote

preparation time 10 minutes (plus standing time)
cooking time 25 minutes
serves 4

¾ cup (75g) rolled rice
1½ cups (375ml) water
1 cup (250ml) skimmed milk

DRIED FRUIT COMPOTE
1 vanilla pod
2½ cups (625ml) water
½ cup (75g) coarsely chopped dried apricots
½ cup (75g) coarsely chopped dried pears
⅓ cup (50g) coarsely chopped dried peaches
2 tablespoons honey
1 teaspoon finely grated lemon rind
1 cinnamon stick

1 Cover rolled rice with the water in small bowl; stand overnight.
2 Make dried fruit compote.
3 Place undrained rolled rice in medium saucepan; cook, stirring, until mixture comes to a boil. Add milk, reduce heat; simmer, uncovered, 10 minutes. Serve with compote.

DRIED FRUIT COMPOTE
Halve vanilla pod lengthways, place in medium saucepan with remaining ingredients; bring to a boil. Reduce heat; simmer, uncovered, 20 minutes. Remove from heat; cool 10 minutes. Remove vanilla pod and cinnamon stick before serving.
TIP Rolled rice is a gluten-free flaked cereal similar to, and a good substitute for, rolled oats. It is available in supermarkets and health-food stores.

per serving 1.9g total fat (0.4g saturated fat); 1028kJ (246 cal); 51.5g carbohydrate; 6.5g protein; 5.9g fibre

sautéed mushrooms on toast

preparation time 10 minutes
cooking time 20 minutes
serves 4

30g butter
200g chestnut mushrooms, sliced thickly
100g fresh shiitake mushrooms, sliced thickly
200g button mushrooms, halved
100g oyster mushrooms, halved
1 clove garlic, crushed
¼ cup (60ml) beef stock
½ loaf ciabatta (220g)
¼ cup coarsely chopped fresh flat-leaf parsley
¼ cup coarsely chopped fresh chives

1 Preheat grill.
2 Melt butter in large frying pan; cook mushrooms and garlic, stirring, about 5 minutes. Add stock; bring to a boil. Reduce heat; simmer, uncovered, about 10 minutes or until mushrooms are cooked as desired.
3 Meanwhile, trim end from bread; cut into eight slices. Toast bread both sides; divide among serving plates.
4 Stir herbs into mushrooms; serve on toast.

per serving 8.1g total fat (4.3g saturated fat); 966kJ (231 cal); 29.7g carbohydrate; 9.8g protein; 6.2g fibre

smoked salmon, cream cheese and rocket bruschetta

preparation time 15 minutes
cooking time 5 minutes
serves 4

⅓ cup (80g) light cream cheese
1 shallot (25g), chopped finely
2 teaspoons lemon juice
½ teaspoon dijon mustard
1 tablespoon drained capers, rinsed, chopped coarsely
1 loaf sourdough bread (675g)
30g baby rocket leaves
200g sliced smoked salmon

1 Preheat grill.
2 Combine cream cheese, shallot, juice, mustard and capers in small bowl.
3 Trim ends from bread, cut into eight slices. Toast bread both sides. Spread cheese mixture over toast; divide among plates. Top with rocket and salmon.

per serving 10.1g total fat (3.3g saturated fat); 2153kJ (515 cal); 77.1g carbohydrate; 28g protein; 8g fibre

bruschetta with strawberry, banana and ricotta

preparation time 15 minutes
cooking time 10 minutes
serves 4

½ loaf ciabatta (220g)
200g low-fat ricotta
2 tablespoons honey
1 teaspoon finely grated orange rind
¼ teaspoon ground cinnamon
125g strawberries, sliced thickly
1 small banana (130g), sliced thinly
2 tablespoons brown sugar

1 Preheat grill.
2 Trim end from bread; cut into eight slices.
3 Beat ricotta, honey, rind and cinnamon in small bowl with electric mixer until smooth.
4 Combine strawberries, banana and sugar in small frying pan; stir gently over low heat until sugar dissolves.
5 Meanwhile, toast bread both sides. Spread with ricotta mixture, divide among plates; top with strawberry mixture.

per serving 5.8g total fat (3g saturated fat); 1208kJ (289 cal); 49g carbohydrate; 10.8g protein; 2.8g fibre

soufflé with berry compote

preparation time 10 minutes
cooking time 15 minutes
serves 4

1 tablespoon caster sugar
2 egg yolks
½ cup (80g) icing sugar
4 egg whites

BERRY COMPOTE
½ cup (75g) frozen mixed berries
2 tablespoons orange juice
1 tablespoon caster sugar

1 Make berry compote.
2 Preheat oven to moderate. Lightly grease four 1¼-cup (310ml) ovenproof dishes; sprinkle insides of dishes evenly with caster sugar, shake away excess. Place dishes on oven tray.
3 Whisk egg yolks and 2 tablespoons of the icing sugar in large bowl until mixture is well combined.
4 Beat the egg whites in small bowl with electric mixer until soft peaks form. With motor operating, gradually add remaining icing sugar, beating until firm peaks form.
5 Gently fold egg-white mixture, in two batches, into yolk mixture; divide mixture among prepared dishes. Bake soufflés, uncovered, in moderate oven about 12 minutes or until puffed and browned lightly. Dust with sifted icing sugar, if desired; serve with compote.

BERRY COMPOTE
Combine ingredients in small saucepan; bring to a boil. Reduce heat; simmer, uncovered, 2 minutes.

per serving 2.7g total fat (0.8g saturated fat); 698kJ (167 cal); 31.5g carbohydrate; 5.4g protein; 0.7g fibre

oaty apple pikelets

preparation time 10 minutes (plus refrigeration time)
cooking time 15 minutes
serves 4

2 cups (500ml) skimmed milk
1 cup (120g) oat bran
½ cup (75g) plain flour
2 tablespoons brown sugar
½ teaspoon mixed spice
2 eggs
1 large apple (200g), peeled, cored, chopped finely
1 tablespoon lemon juice
½ cup (175g) honey
½ cup (100g) low-fat ricotta

1 Blend or process milk, bran, flour, sugar, spice and eggs until smooth; pour into large jug. Stir in apple and juice, cover; refrigerate 30 minutes (mixture will separate during refrigeration).
2 Heat lightly oiled large frying pan. Stir mixture to combine; using ¼-cup batter for each pikelet (mixture will be runny), cook two pikelets at a time, uncovered, until bubbles appear on the surface. Turn; cook until browned lightly. Remove pikelets from pan; cover to keep warm. Repeat with remaining batter to make 12 pikelets.
3 Divide pikelets among plates; top with honey and ricotta.

per serving 7.3g total fat (2.7g saturated fat); 1973kJ (472 cal); 83.6g carbohydrate; 19g protein; 6.3g fibre

day-before ginger muffins with stewed pear

preparation time 25 minutes (plus refrigeration time)
cooking time 30 minutes
makes 6

3 teaspoons ground ginger
⅔ cup (100g) coarsely chopped dried apricots
½ cup (95g) coarsely chopped dried figs
1⅓ cups (95g) All-Bran breakfast cereal
1½ cups (375ml) skimmed milk
1¼ cups (275g) firmly packed brown sugar
⅓ cup (115g) golden syrup
1¼ cups (185g) self-raising flour
¼ cup (35g) toasted pecans, chopped coarsely
3 medium pears (690g), peeled, cut into
8 wedges each
1 cup (250ml) water
1 tablespoon icing sugar

1 Combine ginger, apricot, fig, cereal, milk, brown sugar and half of the golden syrup in large bowl; mix well. Cover; refrigerate overnight.
2 Preheat oven to moderately hot. Lightly grease six-hole (¾-cup/180ml) large muffin tray.
3 Stir flour and nuts into apricot mixture. Spoon mixture into prepared muffin tray; bake, uncovered, in moderately hot oven about 30 minutes. Stand muffins in tray 5 minutes before turning onto wire rack.
4 Meanwhile, combine pear, remaining golden syrup and the water in large frying pan; simmer, covered, about 15 minutes or until pears are soft. Dust muffins with sifted icing sugar; serve with stewed pear.
TIP Make the batter for these muffins the night before you want to bake and serve them.

per muffin 5.7g total fat (0.5g saturated fat); 2383kJ (570 cal); 122.8g carbohydrate; 10.1g protein; 12.9g fibre

maple-syrup-flavoured borlotti beans with bacon

preparation time 10 minutes (plus standing time)
cooking time 1 hour 40 minutes
serves 4

1 cup (200g) dried borlotti beans
3 bacon rashers (210g), rind removed, chopped coarsely
1 medium brown onion (150g), chopped finely
1 clove garlic, crushed
1 tablespoon tomato paste
425g can crushed tomatoes
2 cups (500ml) water
1 tablespoon worcestershire sauce
2 teaspoons dijon mustard
2 tablespoons pure maple syrup

1 Place beans in medium bowl, cover with water; stand overnight.
2 Cook bacon, onion and garlic in lightly oiled large saucepan, stirring, until onion softens. Add rinsed, drained beans, paste, undrained tomatoes, the water, sauce and mustard; bring to a boil. Reduce heat; simmer, covered, about 1½ hours or until beans are just tender. Stir maple syrup into hot beans before serving.
TIP You can soak the beans early in the day before you want to serve them, then at night make this recipe; reheat the beans for breakfast the following day.

per serving 7.6g total fat (2.9g saturated fat); 1032kJ (247 cal); 30.3g carbohydrate; 16.2g protein; 4g fibre

eggs ranchero-style

preparation time 10 minutes
cooking time 30 minutes
serves 4

1 small red onion (100g), chopped finely
4 medium tomatoes (600g), chopped coarsely
2 tablespoons water
1 tablespoon balsamic vinegar
1 medium red pepper (200g), chopped finely
4 eggs
4 corn tortillas

1 Cook onion in lightly oiled large non-stick frying pan, stirring, until softened. Add tomato, the water and vinegar; bring to a boil. Reduce heat; simmer, uncovered, 15 minutes, stirring occasionally. Add pepper; cook, uncovered, 5 minutes.
2 Using large shallow mixing spoon, press four shallow depressions into tomato mixture. Working quickly, break eggs, one at a time, into cup, sliding each egg into one of the hollows in tomato mixture. Cover pan; cook over low heat, about 5 minutes or until eggs are just set.
3 Divide warmed tortillas among plates. Use spatula to carefully lift egg and tomato mixture onto each tortilla.
TIP This is our take on the traditional Mexican breakfast dish, huevos rancheros.

per serving 6g total fat (1.7g saturated fat); 619kJ; (148 cal) 13.1g carbohydrate; 10.1g protein; 3.4g fibre

soups

tofu and spinach miso

preparation time 10 minutes
cooking time 10 minutes
serves 4

1.5 litres (6 cups) water
¼ cup (75g) yellow miso
1 tablespoon japanese soy sauce
3cm piece fresh ginger (15g), grated
100g dried soba noodles
200g marinated tofu, cut into 2cm pieces
4 spring onions, sliced thinly
100g baby spinach leaves
1 fresh long red chilli, sliced thinly

1 Place the water in large saucepan with miso, sauce and ginger; bring to a boil. Add noodles, return to a boil; cook, uncovered, about 3 minutes or until noodles are just tender.
2 Remove from heat, add tofu, onion and spinach to broth; stir gently until spinach just wilts.
3 Serve bowls of soup sprinkled with chilli.

per serving 4.9g total fat (0.7g saturated fat); 803kJ (192 cal); 22.9g carbohydrate; 12.1g protein; 3.8g fibre

slow-cooked lamb and white bean soup

preparation time 35 minutes (plus standing time)
cooking time 3 hours 20 minutes
serves 4

1 cup (200g) dried cannellini beans
2 medium red peppers (400g)
1 tablespoon olive oil
1.5kg french-trimmed lamb shanks
1 large brown onion (200g), chopped coarsely
2 cloves garlic, quartered
2 medium carrots (240g), chopped coarsely
2 trimmed celery stalks (200g), chopped coarsely
2 tablespoons tomato paste
1 cup (250ml) dry red wine
3 litres (12 cups) water
80g baby spinach leaves

1 Place beans in medium bowl, cover with water, stand overnight; drain. Rinse under cold water; drain.
2 Quarter peppers; discard seeds and membranes. Roast under grill or in very hot oven, skin-side up, until skin blisters and blackens. Cover pepper pieces with plastic or paper for 5 minutes; peel away skin, dice pepper finely.
3 Heat oil in large saucepan; cook lamb, in batches, until browned all over. Cook onion and garlic in same pan, stirring, until onion softens. Add carrot and celery; cook, stirring, 2 minutes. Add paste and wine; bring to a boil. Reduce heat; simmer, uncovered, 5 minutes.
4 Return lamb to pan with the water; bring to a boil. Reduce heat; simmer, uncovered, 2 hours, skimming fat from surface occasionally.
5 Meanwhile, place beans in medium saucepan of boiling water; return to a boil. Reduce heat; simmer, uncovered, about 30 minutes or until beans are almost tender. Drain.
6 Remove lamb from pan. Strain broth through muslin-lined sieve or colander into large heatproof bowl; discard solids. When lamb is cool enough to handle, remove meat from shanks; shred coarsely. Discard bones.
7 Return broth to same cleaned pan with pepper, beans and lamb; bring to a boil. Reduce heat; simmer, uncovered, 5 minutes. Remove from heat; stir in spinach.

per serving 1.8g total fat (0.7g saturated fat); 171kJ (41 cal); 1.4g carbohydrate; 3.8g protein; 0.7g fibre

chicken and corn soup

preparation time 5 minutes
cooking time 2 minutes
serves 1

125g can creamed corn
½ cup shredded cooked chicken
1 tablespoon soy sauce
½ teaspoon sambal oelek
375ml carton salt-reduced chicken stock
2 tablespoons fresh flat-leaf parsley leaves

1 Combine all ingredients in medium microwave-safe bowl. Cook, uncovered, on HIGH (100%) in microwave oven about 2 minutes or until hot.
2 Sprinkle with flat-leaf parsley.

per serving 7.4g total fat (2.4g saturated fat); 1024kJ (245 cal); 20.4g carbohydrate; 24g protein; 4g fibre

risoni and spring vegetable soup

preparation time 5 minutes
cooking time 10 minutes
serves 1

¼ cup risoni
2 green beans, thinly sliced
1 small carrot, thinly sliced
375ml carton salt-reduced vegetable stock
1 tablespoon shredded fresh basil

1 Cook risoni in small saucepan of boiling water, uncovered, until almost tender. Add beans and carrot; cook, uncovered, 1 minute. Drain well.
2 Place mixture in medium microwave-safe bowl with stock. Cook, uncovered, on HIGH (100%) in microwave oven about 2 minutes or until hot.
3 Sprinkle with basil.

per serving 2.2g total fat (0.9g saturated fat); 1016kJ (243 cal); 44.2g carbohydrate; 11g protein; 4.6g fibre

french onion soup

preparation time 5 minutes
cooking time 20 minutes
serves 1

1 medium brown onion, thinly sliced
2 teaspoons olive oil
2 teaspoons brown sugar
375ml carton salt-reduced beef stock
1 teaspoon coarsely chopped fresh chives

1 Cook onion in oil in small frying pan, stirring, until onion softens. Add sugar, then continue to cook, stirring occasionally, about 10 minutes or until onion caramelises.
2 Add stock. Cook, stirring occasionally, for about 5 minutes or until hot.
3 Sprinkle with chives.

per serving 10g total fat (1.7g saturated fat); 702kJ (168 cal); 13.6g carbohydrate; 6.5g protein; 1.8g fibre

thai chicken noodle soup

preparation time 5 minutes
cooking time 2 minutes
serves 1

½ cup thinly sliced cooked chicken
1 teaspoon red curry paste
175g packet singapore noodles
375ml carton salt-reduced chicken stock
1 tablespoon coarsely chopped fresh coriander
½ spring onion, thinly sliced

1 At home, combine chicken and curry paste.
2 Rinse noodles under hot water. Place noodles in medium microwave-safe bowl with chicken mixture and stock.
3 Cook, uncovered, on HIGH (100%) in microwave oven about 2 minutes or until hot.
4 Sprinkle with coriander and spring onion.

per serving 10.4g total fat (2.8g saturated fat); 2617kJ (626 cal); 94g carbohydrate; 37.7g protein; 24.4g fibre

minestrone

preparation time 40 minutes (plus refrigeration time)
cooking time 3 hours 35 minutes serves 6

2 ham hocks (1kg)
1 medium brown onion (150g), quartered
1 trimmed celery stalk (100g), chopped coarsely
1 teaspoon black peppercorns
1 bay leaf
4 litres (16 cups) water
1 tablespoon olive oil
2 trimmed celery stalks (200g), chopped finely
1 large carrot (180g), chopped finely
3 cloves garlic, crushed
¼ cup (70g) tomato paste
2 large tomatoes (440g), chopped finely
1 small leek (200g), sliced thinly
1 cup (100g) small pasta shells
420g can white beans, rinsed, drained
½ cup coarsely chopped fresh flat-leaf parsley
½ cup coarsely chopped fresh basil
½ cup (40g) shaved parmesan cheese

1 Preheat oven to 220°C/200°C fan-assisted.
2 Roast hocks and onion in baking dish, uncovered, 30 minutes. Combine with coarsely chopped celery, peppercorns, bay leaf and the water in large saucepan; bring to a boil. Simmer, uncovered, 2 hours.
3 Remove hocks from soup. Strain broth through muslin-lined sieve or colander into large heatproof bowl; discard solids. Allow broth to cool, cover; refrigerate until cold. When cool, remove ham from bones; shred coarsely. Discard bones.
4 Meanwhile, heat oil in large saucepan; cook finely chopped celery and carrot, stirring, 2 minutes. Add ham, garlic, paste and tomato; cook, stirring, 2 minutes.
5 Discard fat from surface of broth. Place broth in measuring jug; add enough water to make 2 litres. Add broth to pan; bring to a boil. Simmer, covered, 20 minutes.
6 Add leek, pasta and beans; bring to a boil. Simmer, uncovered, until pasta is just tender. Remove from heat; stir in herbs. Serve soup sprinkled with cheese.
TIP You can make the broth either the day before or in the morning of the day you want to finish preparing the minestrone so that it chills long enough for the fat to solidify on top; skim it away before reheating the broth.

per serving 7.2g total fat (2.4g saturated fat); 865kJ (207 cal); 19.6g carbohydrate; 12.7g protein; 6.1g fibre

light meals and snacks

lentil, beetroot and rocket salad

preparation time 10 minutes
serves 1

½ cup cooked brown lentils
½ cup drained canned baby beetroot halves
1½ cups trimmed baby rocket leaves
30g feta cheese, crumbled

BALSAMIC DRESSING
1 tablespoon balsamic vinegar
1 teaspoon olive oil

1 Combine lentils and beetroot halves in a medium bowl.
2 For dressing, combine balsamic vinegar and olive oil in a small bowl; toss dressing with salad.
3 Serve on baby rocket leaves; top with feta cheese.

per serving 12.6g total fat (5.3g saturated fat); 1041kJ (249 cal); 19.2g carbohydrate; 15.1g protein; 7g fibre

chicken and peach salad

preparation time 10 minutes
serves 1

80g shredded cooked chicken
1½ cups shredded chinese cabbage
¼ cup shredded fresh mint leaves
1 small peach, cut into wedges

LIME DRESSING
2 tablespoons lime juice
1 teaspoon olive oil

1 Combine chicken, chinese cabbage, fresh mint leaves and peach wedges in a medium bowl.
2 For dressing, combine lime juice and olive oil in a small bowl; toss dressing with salad.

per serving 11.3g total fat (2.4g saturated fat); 974kJ (233 cal); 8.5g carbohydrate; 22.9g protein; 4.4g fibre

chickpea salad

preparation time 15 minutes
serves 1

½ cup canned chickpeas, rinsed, drained
½ cucumber, coarsely chopped
½ small red onion, thinly sliced
¼ cup pitted kalamata olives
⅓ cup fresh flat-leaf parsley leaves
¼ cup coarsely chopped yellow pepper
1 small plum tomato, deseeded and cut into wedges
2 tablespoons prepared low-fat tzatziki

LEMON DRESSING
1 tablespoon lemon juice
1 teaspoon olive oil
¼ teaspoon finely chopped lemon rind
¼ teaspoon ground cumin

1 Combine chickpeas, cucumber, onion, olives, flat-leaf parsley, pepper and tomato in a medium bowl.
2 For dressing, combine lemon juice, olive oil, lemon rind and cumin in a small bowl; toss dressing with salad.
3 Top with tzatziki.

per serving 8.5g total fat (1.6g saturated fat); 1195kJ (286 cal); 9.8g carbohydrate; 11.4g protein; 9g fibre

tuna salad

preparation time 5 minutes
serves 1

125g can sliced tuna in springwater, drained
2 cups baby spinach leaves, trimmed
1½ teaspoons baby capers, rinsed, drained
⅓ cup cherry tomatoes, halved
3 teaspoons fresh dill sprigs
LEMON DRESSING
1 tablespoon lemon juice
1 teaspoon olive oil

1 Combine tuna, spinach leaves, capers, tomatoes and dill sprigs in a medium bowl.
2 For dressing, combine lemon juice and olive oil in a small bowl; toss dressing with salad.

per serving 7.5g total fat (1.7g saturated fat); 798kJ (191 cal); 3.4g carbohydrate; 27.1g protein; 2.8g fibre

pea, ricotta, mint and spinach sandwich

preparation time 10 minutes
cooking time 5 minutes
serves 1

¼ cup frozen peas
50g low-fat ricotta
1 tablespoon lemon juice
1 tablespoon finely chopped fresh mint
2 slices soy and linseed bread
a few spinach leaves

1 Boil, steam or microwave peas until tender; drain.
2 Cool, then, using fork, lightly crush peas. Combine pea mash with ricotta, lemon juice and mint.
3 Spread pea mixture on one slice bread; top with a few spinach leaves, then sandwich together with another slice of bread.

per serving 9g total fat (3.4g saturated fat); 1195kJ (286 cal); 33.2g carbohydrate; 18.1g protein; 7.9g fibre

prawn and lime mayonnaise bruschetta

preparation time 10 minutes
cooking time 2 minutes
serves 1

2 slices ciabatta bread
10g baby rocket leaves
8 cooked small prawns
LIME MAYONNAISE
2 tablespoons low-fat mayonnaise
2 teaspoons finely chopped fresh dill
1 tablespoon lime juice

1 Make lime mayonnaise by combining mayonnaise, dill and lime juice in a small bowl.
2 Toast ciabatta; divide rocket leaves, small prawns and mayonnaise mixture between both slices.

per serving 7.6g total fat (1.4g saturated fat); 1158kJ (277 cal); 39.2g carbohydrate; 11.9g protein; 2.5g fibre

ham, tomato and avocado bruschetta

preparation time 5 minutes
cooking time 25 minutes
serves 1

1 medium plum tomato, halved
2 teaspoons brown sugar
2 slices ciabatta bread
¼ small avocado
50g shaved ham
pepper

1 Preheat oven to moderate.
2 Place tomato halves, cut-side up, on baking tray, sprinkle with sugar; cook, uncovered, in moderate oven for 20 minutes.
3 Toast ciabatta; divide avocado, ham and tomato halves between slices. Sprinkle with pepper, if desired.

per serving 11.6g total fat (2.7g saturated fat); 1367kJ (327 cal); 39.1g carbohydrate; 16.6g protein; 3.4g fibre

tuna salad bruschetta

preparation time 5 minutes
cooking time 2 minutes
serves 1

95g can tuna in brine, drained
1 tablespoon low-fat mayonnaise
½ small red onion, finely chopped
1 tablespoon coarsely chopped fresh
flat-leaf parsley
2 slices ciabatta bread

1 Combine tuna, mayonnaise, onion and flat-leaf
parsley in a small bowl.
2 Toast ciabatta; divide tuna salad between slices.

per serving 6.5g total fat (1.6g saturated fat); 1304kJ
(312 cal); 37g carbohydrate; 25.9g protein; 3g fibre

smoked chicken and mango chutney bruschetta

preparation time 5 minutes
cooking time 2 minutes
serves 1

2 slices ciabatta bread
1 teaspoon low-fat mayonnaise
100g smoked chicken, thinly sliced
10g mixed salad leaves
1 tablespoon mango chutney

1 Toast ciabatta.
2 Spread mayonnaise over both slices, then divide
chicken, salad leaves and mango chutney between
both slices.

per serving 9.6g total fat (2.4g saturated fat); 1605kJ
(384 cal); 43.2g carbohydrate; 30.8g protein; 2.8g fibre

lamb, tabbouleh and hummus on pitta

preparation time 5 minutes
serves 1

1 pocket pitta
1 tablespoon ready-made hummus
¼ cup ready-made tabbouleh
50g sliced roast lamb
¼ cup baby rocket leaves, trimmed

1 Separate one pocket pitta into halves.
2 Spread hummus on inside of one half of pitta, then top with tabbouleh, lamb, rocket leaves and remaining half of pitta.

per serving 14.6g total fat (4.3g saturated fat);
1772kJ (424 cal); 48.2g carbohydrate; 24.7g protein; 5.9g fibre

roast beef and horseradish cream on focaccia

preparation time 5 minutes
serves 1

1 small focaccia
2 teaspoons horseradish cream
50g sliced roast beef
¼ cup char-grilled pepper, thickly sliced
¼ cup baby rocket leaves, trimmed

1 Split focaccia in half horizontally.
2 Spread horseradish cream on cut-side of one half of focaccia, then top with beef, pepper, rocket leaves and remaining half of focaccia.

per serving 11.4g total fat (2.8g saturated fat); 2165kJ (518 cal); 72.5g carbohydrate; 29.6g protein; 10.6g fibre

smoked trout salad roll

preparation time 5 minutes
serves 1

1 wholemeal roll
50g smoked trout, flaked
1 tablespoon light soured cream
1 tablespoon finely chopped cornichons
1 tablespoon finely chopped fresh dill
1 tablespoon lemon juice

1 Split roll in half horizontally.
2 Combine trout, cream, cornichons, dill and lemon juice in a small bowl.
3 Spread one half of roll with trout mixture. Top with remaining half of roll.

per serving 9.4g total fat (3.7g saturated fat); 1350kJ (323 cal); 37.5g carbohydrate; 21.2g protein; 7g fibre

spicy parmesan seed twists

preparation time 15 minutes
cooking time 15 minutes
makes 24

1 sheet ready-rolled puff pastry, halved
1 egg yolk
1 tablespoon poppy seeds
2 teaspoons mustard seeds
1 teaspoon sweet paprika
½ teaspoon salt
2 tablespoons finely grated parmesan cheese

1 Preheat oven to moderately hot. Grease and line two oven trays.
2 Brush pastry halves with egg on one side; sprinkle with combined seeds, paprika and salt. Turn over one of the halves so unseeded side faces up; brush with egg, sprinkle with parmesan. Sandwich the two halves with parmesan side in the centre and two seeded sides facing out; press down firmly.
3 Cut pastry widthways into 24 strips; twist each strip, pinching ends to seal. Place twists on prepared trays; bake, uncovered, in moderately hot oven about 15 minutes or until browned lightly.

per twist 2.2g total fat (1.1g saturated fat); 138kJ (33 cal); 2.5g carbohydrate; 0.8g protein; 0.2g fibre

polenta and cottage cheese muffins

preparation time 20 minutes
cooking time 20 minutes
makes 12

2 cups (300g) self-raising flour
2 teaspoons caster sugar
½ cup (85g) polenta
250g low-fat cottage cheese
⅓ cup (25g) coarsely grated parmesan cheese
½ teaspoon dried chilli flakes
4 spring onions, chopped finely
1 egg
1 cup (250ml) skimmed milk
2 tablespoons vegetable oil

1 Preheat oven to moderately hot. Lightly grease 12-hole (⅓-cup/80ml) muffin tray.
2 Combine flour, sugar and ⅓ cup of the polenta in medium bowl with cottage cheese, parmesan, chilli and onion. Stir in combined egg, milk and oil. Divide mixture among prepared holes of muffin pan; sprinkle with remaining polenta.
3 Bake, uncovered, in moderately hot oven about 20 minutes. Stand muffins in pan 5 minutes; turn onto wire rack to cool.

per muffin 5.2g total fat (1.4g saturated fat); 796kJ (184 cal); 25.8g carbohydrate; 8.5g protein; 1.2g fibre

main courses

barley risotto with chicken and tarragon

preparation time 15 minutes
cooking time 40 minutes
serves 4

1 tablespoon olive oil
500g chicken breast fillets, sliced thinly
3 cups (750ml) chicken stock
2 cups (500ml) water
1 medium brown onion (150g), chopped finely
1 clove garlic, crushed
2 medium leeks (700g), sliced thinly
¾ cup (150g) pearl barley
  cup (80ml) dry white wine
1 cup (120g) frozen peas
2 tablespoons finely shredded fresh tarragon

1 Heat half of the oil in large saucepan; cook chicken, in batches, until browned lightly and cooked through. Cover to keep warm.
2 Meanwhile, combine stock and the water in large saucepan; bring to a boil. Reduce heat; simmer, covered.
3 Meanwhile, heat remaining oil in cleaned pan; cook onion, garlic and leek, stirring, until onion softens. Add barley; stir to combine with onion mixture. Add wine; cook, stirring, until almost evaporated. Stir in ½ cup of the simmering stock mixture; cook, stirring, over low heat until liquid is absorbed. Continue adding stock mixture, in ½-cup batches, stirring until absorbed after each addition. Total cooking time should be about 30 minutes or until barley is just tender.
4 Add chicken and peas to risotto; cook, stirring, until peas are just tender. Remove from heat; stir in tarragon.
TIP Pearl barley is barley that has had the husk removed, then been hulled and polished, much the same as rice.

per serving 9.7g total fat (1.9g saturated fat); 1584kJ (379 cal); 31.6g carbohydrate; 38g protein; 9.8g fibre

sweet potato gnocchi with rocket and basil pesto

preparation time 45 minutes (plus refrigeration time)
cooking time 25 minutes
serves 4

2 medium unpeeled sweet potatoes (800g)
4 small unpeeled desiree potatoes (480g)
1 cup (150g) plain flour
1 egg yolk
ROCKET AND BASIL PESTO
2 tablespoons olive oil
2 tablespoons finely grated parmesan cheese
1 clove garlic, quartered
2 tablespoons lemon juice
50g baby rocket leaves
1 cup firmly packed fresh basil leaves

1 Boil sweet potatoes and potatoes, separately, until tender; drain. Peel when cool enough to handle; chop coarsely. Using wooden spoon, push sweet potato and potato through fine sieve into a large bowl.
2 Stir flour and yolk into potato mixture then knead gently on floured surface to form a dough. Divide into four; roll each piece into 40cm log, cut each log into 24 pieces. Roll each piece into a ball; roll balls along the inside tines of a floured fork, pressing gently to form gnocchi shape (grooved one side, dimpled on the other). Place gnocchi, in single layer, on lightly floured trays, cover; refrigerate 1 hour.
3 Place ingredients for rocket and basil pesto in blender or processor; process until smooth.
4 Cook gnocchi, in batches, in large uncovered pan of boiling water about 3 minutes until gnocchi float to surface. Remove gnocchi with slotted spoon. Gently toss with pesto; serve topped with baby rocket leaves.

per serving 12.6g total fat (2.5g saturated fat); 1914kJ (458 cal); 71.8g carbohydrate; 13.4g protein; 8g fibre

pappardelle with roasted tomato, spinach and ricotta

preparation time 10 minutes
cooking time 25 minutes
serves 4

¼ cup (60ml) balsamic vinegar
3 cloves garlic, crushed
4 medium tomatoes (600g), cut into eight wedges
375g pappardelle
100g baby spinach leaves, trimmed
2 tablespoons olive oil
200g low-fat ricotta

1 Preheat oven to moderately hot.
2 Combine vinegar and garlic in small jug. Place tomato, in single layer, on oven tray; pour vinegar mixture over tomato. Roast, uncovered, in moderately hot oven about 25 minutes or until tomato is browned lightly and softened.
3 Meanwhile, cook pasta in large saucepan of boiling water, uncovered, until just tender.
4 Combine drained pasta, tomato, spinach and oil in large bowl. Break ricotta into approximately 3cm pieces; add to pasta mixture, toss gently to combine.
TIP A wide, ribbon-like pasta with scalloped sides, pappardelle is sometimes sold as lasagnette or even lasagne. Any wide, long pasta can be used for this recipe.

per serving 14.8g total fat (4.3g saturated fat); 2057kJ (492 cal); 70.5g carbohydrate; 17.8g protein; 7.7g fibre

chicken, caramelised onion and fig pizza

preparation time 30 minutes (plus standing time)
cooking time 55 minutes
serves 4

200g chicken breast fillet
2 teaspoons olive oil
2 cloves garlic, crushed
425g can crushed tomatoes
1 tablespoon polenta
100g firm goat's cheese
4 large fresh figs (320g), quartered
50g baby rocket leaves

PIZZA DOUGH

2 teaspoons (7g) instant yeast
½ teaspoon salt
2½ cups (375g) plain flour
1 cup (250ml) warm water
2 teaspoons olive oil

CARAMELISED ONION

1 tablespoon olive oil
3 large brown onions (600g), sliced thinly
2 tablespoons brown sugar
2 tablespoons balsamic vinegar

1 Make pizza dough. Make caramelised onion.
2 Preheat oven to moderately hot.
3 Cook chicken in heated lightly oiled small frying pan until cooked through. Cool 10 minutes; slice thinly.
4 Meanwhile, heat oil in small saucepan; cook garlic, stirring, until fragrant. Add undrained tomatoes; bring to a boil. Reduce heat; simmer, uncovered, about 15 minutes or until mixture thickens.
5 Sprinkle polenta onto two 30cm pizza trays. Halve pizza dough; roll each half on lightly floured surface to form 30cm-round pizza base. Place one base on each prepared tray; divide tomato sauce and caramelised onion between bases.
6 Cook pizzas, uncovered, in moderately hot oven about 10 minutes. Divide chicken, cheese and fig between pizzas; cook, uncovered, in moderately hot oven about 5 minutes or until bases are crisp. Sprinkle each with baby rocket leaves before serving.

PIZZA DOUGH

Combine yeast, salt and flour in large bowl; gradually stir in the water and oil. Turn dough onto lightly floured surface; knead until smooth. Place dough in lightly oiled large bowl; cover tightly with cling film then a tea towel. Stand in warm place about 45 minutes or until dough doubles in size. Knead dough gently on floured surface until smooth.

CARAMELISED ONION

Heat oil in large frying pan; cook onion, stirring, until softened. Add sugar and vinegar; cook, stirring occasionally, about 15 minutes or until onion caramelises.

per serving 16.2g total fat; (4.4g saturated fat); 2663kJ (637 cal); 92g carbohydrate; 30.1g protein; 9.6g fibre

beetroot risotto with rocket

preparation time 30 minutes
cooking time 45 minutes
serves 4

2 medium beetroot (350g), peeled, grated coarsely
3 cups (750ml) vegetable stock
3 cups (750ml) water
1 tablespoon olive oil
1 large brown onion (200g), chopped finely
2 cloves garlic, crushed
1½ cups (300g) arborio rice
¼ cup (20g) coarsely grated parmesan cheese
50g baby rocket leaves
1 tablespoon finely chopped fresh flat-leaf parsley

1 Combine beetroot, stock and the water in large saucepan; bring to a boil. Reduce heat; simmer, uncovered.
2 Meanwhile, heat oil in large saucepan; cook onion and garlic, stirring, until onion softens. Add rice; stir rice to coat in onion mixture. Stir in 1 cup simmering beetroot mixture; cook, stirring, over low heat until liquid is absorbed. Continue adding beetroot mixture, in 1-cup batches, stirring, until liquid is absorbed after each addition. Total cooking time should be about 35 minutes or until rice is just tender; gently stir in parmesan cheese.
3 Serve beetroot risotto topped with combined rocket and parsley.

per serving 7.6g total fat (2.1g saturated fat); 1643kJ (393 cal); 69.4g carbohydrate; 11.5g protein; 4.1g fibre

pumpkin and split pea tagine

preparation time 15 minutes
cooking time 40 minutes
serves 4

1 cup (200g) green split peas
1 tablespoon olive oil
1 medium brown onion (150g), chopped finely
2 cloves garlic, crushed
2 teaspoons ground coriander
2 teaspoons ground cumin
2 teaspoons ground ginger
1 teaspoon sweet paprika
1 teaspoon ground allspice
1kg pumpkin, diced into 3cm pieces
425g can crushed tomatoes
1 cup (250ml) water
1 cup (250ml) vegetable stock
2 tablespoons honey
200g green beans, trimmed, chopped coarsely
¼ cup coarsely chopped fresh coriander

1 Cook split peas in medium saucepan of boiling water, uncovered, until just tender; drain. Rinse under cold water; drain.
2 Meanwhile, heat oil in large saucepan; cook onion, stirring, until softened. Add garlic and spices; cook, stirring, about 2 minutes or until fragrant. Add pumpkin; stir pumpkin to coat in spice mixture.
3 Stir in undrained tomatoes, the water and stock; bring to a boil. Reduce heat; simmer, uncovered, about 20 minutes or until pumpkin is just tender. Stir in honey then beans and split peas, reduce heat; simmer, uncovered, about 10 minutes or until beans are just tender. Remove from heat; stir in coriander. Serve with steamed couscous, if desired.

per serving 7g total fat (1.5g saturated fat); 1484kJ (355 cal); 54.5g carbohydrate; 19.1g protein; 11g fibre

koshari

preparation time 15 minutes
cooking time 45 minutes
serves 4

2 cups (400g) brown lentils
¾ cup (150g) white long-grain rice
1 cup coarsely chopped fresh flat-leaf parsley

CARAMELISED ONION

2 tablespoons olive oil
5 large brown onions (1kg), sliced thinly
1½ teaspoons ground allspice
1 teaspoon ground coriander
2 teaspoons white sugar

TOMATO CHILLI SAUCE

2 teaspoons olive oil
3 cloves garlic, crushed
½ teaspoon ground cumin
½ teaspoon dried chilli flakes
⅓ cup (80ml) white vinegar
415ml can tomato juice

1 Make caramelised onion. Make tomato chilli sauce.
2 Meanwhile, cook lentils in medium saucepan of boiling water, uncovered, until just tender; drain.
3 Cook rice in medium saucepan of boiling water, uncovered, until just tender; drain.
4 Remove half of the caramelised onion from pan, reserve. Add lentils and rice to pan, stirring, until heated through. Remove from heat; stir in half of the parsley.
5 Divide koshari among bowls; top with reserved caramelised onion, remaining parsley and tomato chilli sauce.

CARAMELISED ONION

Heat oil in large frying pan; cook onion, allspice and coriander, stirring, until onion softens. Add sugar; cook, uncovered, stirring occasionally, about 30 minutes or until onion caramelises.

TOMATO CHILLI SAUCE

Heat oil in small saucepan; cook garlic, cumin and chilli, stirring, until fragrant. Add vinegar and juice; bring to a boil. Boil, uncovered, 2 minutes.

TIP Various combinations of rice and lentils are eaten throughout the Middle East and India, with perhaps the two most well-known versions being Lebanese mujadara and Indian kitcheree. Our Egyptian take on this homely dish, however, adds delicious 'oomph' to the rice-lentil theme with its fragrantly spicy caramelised onion and piquant chilli sauce.

per serving 13.9g total fat (2g saturated fat); 2416kJ (578 cal); 83.3g carbohydrate; 31.3g protein; 18.8g fibre

harissa-scented lamb with char-grilled vegetables

preparation time 20 minutes
cooking time 30 minutes
serves 6

3 cloves garlic, crushed
1 tablespoon finely grated lemon rind
2 tablespoons harissa
⅓ cup (80ml) lemon juice
1.5kg butterflied leg of lamb, trimmed
2 medium red peppers (400g), sliced thickly
3 large courgettes (450g), sliced thickly
8 baby aubergines (480g), sliced thickly
1 teaspoon ground cumin
1 tablespoon fresh thyme leaves
½ cup coarsely chopped fresh mint

GARLIC SAUCE
1 clove garlic, crushed
1 teaspoon ground cumin
½ cup (125ml) buttermilk
⅓ cup (95g) low-fat yogurt

1 Combine garlic sauce ingredients in screw-top jar; shake well.

2 Combine crushed garlic, rind, harissa and half of the juice in large bowl, add lamb; toss lamb to coat in mixture.

3 Cook lamb on heated lightly oiled grill plate (or grill or barbecue), covered, about 20 minutes or until lamb is cooked as desired. Cover lamb; stand 5 minutes before slicing thickly.

4 Meanwhile, combine pepper, courgette, aubergine, cumin and remaining juice in large bowl. Cook vegetables on same grill plate (or grill or barbecue) until just tender. Return vegetables to bowl with herbs; toss gently to combine.

5 Serve lamb with char-grilled vegetables; drizzle with garlic sauce.

TIP Harissa, a Moroccan sauce or paste made from dried red chillies, garlic oil and caraway seeds, can be used as a rub for meat, an ingredient in sauces and dressings, or eaten on its own as a condiment. It is available commercially from supermarkets.

per serving 7g total fat (3g saturated fat); 1780kJ (354 cal); 9.7g carbohydrate; 61.6g protein; 4.3g fibre

chilli coriander lamb with barley salad

preparation time 20 minutes
cooking time 30 minutes
serves 4

1 tablespoon coriander seeds, crushed lightly
½ teaspoon dried chilli flakes
2 cloves garlic, crushed
4 lamb fillets (800g)
1 cup (200g) pearl barley
¼ teaspoon ground turmeric
⅓ cup coarsely chopped fresh mint
⅓ cup coarsely chopped fresh coriander
1 small red onion (100g), chopped finely
250g cherry tomatoes, quartered
¼ cup (60ml) lemon juice
2 teaspoons olive oil

1 Combine seeds, chilli and garlic in medium bowl, add lamb; toss lamb to coat in mixture. Cover; refrigerate until required.
2 Meanwhile, cook barley in large saucepan of boiling water, uncovered, about 20 minutes or until just tender; drain. Rinse under cold water; drain.
3 Cook lamb on heated lightly oiled grill plate (or grill or barbecue) until cooked as desired. Cover lamb; stand 5 minutes before slicing thickly.
4 Combine remaining ingredients in large bowl, add barley; toss gently to combine. Serve salad with lamb.

per serving 10.9g total fat (3.8g saturated fat); 1822kJ (436 cal); 33.8g carbohydrate; 49.2g protein; 7.8g fibre

orange-glazed pork cutlets with spinach and pecan salad

preparation time 20 minutes
cooking time 20 minutes
serves 4

½ cup (125ml) orange juice
¼ cup (55g) white sugar
2 cloves garlic, crushed
4 pork cutlets (950g), trimmed

SPINACH AND PECAN SALAD
150g baby spinach leaves
¼ cup (35g) toasted pecans, chopped coarsely
150g mangetout, trimmed, halved
4 medium oranges (960g)

CITRUS DRESSING
2 tablespoons orange juice
1 tablespoon lemon juice
½ teaspoon dijon mustard
½ teaspoon white sugar
2 teaspoons olive oil

1 Combine juice, sugar and garlic in small saucepan, bring to a boil. Reduce heat; simmer, without stirring, about 10 minutes or until glaze reduces to about ⅓ cup.
2 Brush cutlets both sides with glaze; cook, uncovered, in heated lightly oiled large frying pan about 10 minutes or until cooked as desired, brushing frequently with remaining glaze. Cover to keep warm.
3 Meanwhile, make spinach and pecan salad.
4 Place citrus dressing ingredients in screw-top jar; shake well. Pour dressing over salad; toss gently to combine. Serve salad with cutlets.

SPINACH AND PECAN SALAD
Combine spinach, nuts and mangetout in large bowl. Segment peeled oranges over salad to catch juice; add segments to salad, toss gently to combine.

per serving 17g total fat (3.8g saturated fat); 1935kJ (463 cal); 33.2g carbohydrate; 44.1g protein; 6.4g fibre

layered vine leaves with aubergine and lamb

preparation time 20 minutes
cooking time 20 minutes
serves 4

2 large red peppers (700g)
1 medium aubergine (300g), cut crossways
into 12 slices
1 medium brown onion (150g), chopped finely
1 clove garlic, crushed
500g minced lamb
2 teaspoons baharat
1 tablespoon brandy
1 tablespoon tomato paste
½ cup (125ml) beef stock
1 tablespoon lime juice
1 tablespoon toasted pine nuts
1 cup coarsely chopped fresh flat-leaf parsley
8 fresh vine leaves

1 Quarter peppers; remove seeds and membrane. Place peppers, skin-side up, and aubergine on lightly oiled oven tray under preheated grill or in preheated hot oven until skin blisters. Cover peppers with cling film or paper for 5 minutes; peel away skin, then slice thinly.
2 Meanwhile, cook onion and garlic in heated lightly oiled large frying pan, stirring, until onion just softens. Add mince and spice; cook, stirring, until mince changes colour. Stir in combined brandy, paste and stock; bring to a boil. Reduce heat; simmer, uncovered, stirring, about 2 minutes or until liquid reduces by half. Remove from heat; stir in juice, nuts and parsley. Cover to keep warm.
3 Place vine leaves in large saucepan of boiling water, uncovered, for about 30 seconds or just until pliable; drain, in single layer, on absorbent paper.
4 Place one leaf on each plate; layer each leaf with one slice of aubergine, a few pepper slices, ¼ cup mince mixture and another vine leaf. Repeat layering with remaining aubergine, pepepr and mince.
TIPS Baharat is an aromatic all-purpose spice blend used throughout the Middle East. It is often sold as lebanese seven-spice, and can be found at Middle-Eastern food stores, some delicatessens and specialist food shops. Make a substitute for baharat by combining 2 teaspoons paprika, 1 tablespoon ground cumin, 1 tablespoon ground coriander, 1 crushed clove and ½ teaspoon ground nutmeg.
If fresh vine leaves are unavailable, buy those preserved in brine and sold in vacuum packs. Rinse thoroughly under cold water, then follow step 3 above, reducing time in the boiling water to 10 seconds.

per serving 15.5g total fat (5.9g saturated fat); 1321kJ (316 cal); 10.4g carbohydrate; 31.1g protein; 5.6g fibre

shredded chicken salad

preparation time 25 minutes
cooking time 10 minutes
serves 4

500g chicken breast fillets
125g rice vermicelli
1 large carrot (180g), cut into matchsticks
1 medium red pepper (200g), sliced thinly
1 medium green pepper (200g), sliced thinly
½ cucumber (130g), deseeded, sliced thinly
1 fresh long red chilli, sliced thinly
1 cup coarsely shredded fresh mint
¼ cup (35g) toasted unsalted peanuts,
chopped coarsely

LIME AND PALM SUGAR DRESSING
¼ cup (60ml) lime juice
¼ cup (65g) grated palm sugar
¼ cup (60ml) fish sauce

1 Place lime and palm sugar dressing ingredients in screw-top jar; shake well.
2 Place chicken and half of the dressing in medium saucepan with barely enough boiling water to cover chicken; bring to a boil. Reduce heat; simmer, uncovered, about 10 minutes or until chicken is cooked through. Cool chicken in poaching liquid 10 minutes; discard liquid (or reserve for another use). Using two forks, shred chicken finely.
3 Meanwhile, place vermicelli in large heatproof bowl; cover with boiling water. Stand until just tender; drain. Rinse under cold water; drain.
4 Place chicken and vermicelli in large bowl with carrot, peppers, cucumber, chilli, mint and remaining dressing; toss gently to combine. Divide salad among plates; top with nuts.

per serving 7.8g total fat (1.3g saturated fat); 1613kJ (386 cal); 43.1g carbohydrate; 35.6g protein; 4.6g fibre

thai pork salad with kaffir lime dressing

preparation time 15 minutes
cooking time 15 minutes
serves 4

600g pork fillets
2 tablespoons grated palm sugar
1 tablespoon finely grated lime rind
2 teaspoons groudnut oil
350g watercress, trimmed
1 cup loosely packed fresh thai basil leaves
½ cup loosely packed fresh coriander leaves
½ cup loosely packed fresh mint leaves
1½ cups (120g) beansprouts
1 medium green pepper (200g), sliced thinly

KAFFIR LIME DRESSING
2 cloves garlic, crushed
3 shallots (75g), sliced thinly
1 fresh small red thai chilli, sliced thinly
3 fresh kaffir lime leaves, sliced thinly
¼ cup (60ml) lime juice
⅓ cup (80ml) fish sauce
2 teaspoons grated palm sugar

1 Cut pork fillets in half horizontally. Combine sugar, rind and oil in large bowl, add pork; toss pork to coat in mixture. Cook pork, in batches, in heated lightly oiled large frying pan, over medium heat, about 15 minutes or until cooked as desired. Cover pork; stand 5 minutes, then slice thinly.
2 Meanwhile, place kaffir lime dressing ingredients in screw-top jar; shake well.
3 Place pork in large bowl with remaining ingredients, add dressing; toss gently to combine.

per serving 6.4g total fat (1.6g saturated fat); 1104kJ (264 cal); 12.2g carbohydrate; 38.8g protein; 5.8g fibre

veal, mushroom and fennel rolls with horseradish mash

preparation time 30 minutes
cooking time 35 minutes
serves 4

1 tablespoon olive oil
2 cloves garlic, crushed
2 small fennel bulbs (400g), sliced thinly
3 flat mushrooms (240g), sliced thickly
½ cup (125ml) dry white wine
1½ cups (375ml) chicken stock
6 veal steaks (600g)
1 tablespoon finely chopped fresh flat-leaf parsley

HORSERADISH MASH

800g medium potatoes, chopped coarsely
2 tablespoons horseradish cream
¾ cup (180ml) hot skimmed milk
2 tablespoons finely chopped fresh flat-leaf parsley

1 Heat half of the oil in large frying pan; cook garlic and fennel, stirring, until fennel browns lightly. Add mushroom, half of the wine and ½ cup of the stock; bring to a boil. Reduce heat; simmer, uncovered, about 15 minutes or until liquid has evaporated. Cool 10 minutes.
2 Meanwhile, using meat mallet, gently pound veal steaks, one at a time, between pieces of cling film until about 5mm thick; cut each piece in half crossways.
3 Divide fennel mixture among veal pieces; roll to enclose filling, securing each roll with a toothpick.
4 Make horseradish mash.
5 Heat remaining oil in large frying pan; cook rolls, uncovered, until cooked as desired. Cover to keep warm. Place remaining wine in same pan; bring to a boil, stirring. Boil 2 minutes then add remaining stock; bring to a boil, stirring. Boil, uncovered, 5 minutes.
6 Serve veal rolls with mash and sauce, sprinkled with parsley.

HORSERADISH MASH

Boil, steam or microwave potato; drain. Mash potato in large bowl; stir in horseradish and milk then parsley.

per serving 10.3g total fat (2.6g saturated fat); 1731kJ (414 cal); 30.2g carbohydrate; 44.1g protein; 6.6g fibre

honey dijon chicken with creamy celery and fennel slaw

preparation time 20 minutes
cooking time 30 minutes
serves 4

2 tablespoons honey
2 teaspoons dijon mustard
4 chicken breast fillets (680g)
CREAMY FENNEL AND CELERY SLAW
2 medium fennel bulbs (600g)
3 trimmed celery stalks (300g), sliced thinly
¼ cup coarsely chopped fresh flat-leaf parsley
2 teaspoons dijon mustard
2 tablespoons lemon juice
2 tablespoons light soured cream
2 cloves garlic, crushed
¼ cup (75g) low-fat mayonnaise

1 Combine honey and mustard in small bowl. Brush chicken both sides with half of the honey mixture; cook, in batches, in heated lightly oiled large frying pan about 15 minutes or until cooked through, brushing with remaining honey mixture.
2 Meanwhile, make creamy fennel and celery slaw.
3 Serve chicken with slaw, sprinkled with reserved fennel tips.

CREAMY FENNEL AND CELERY SLAW
Trim fennel, reserving about 1 tablespoon of the tips (discard the rest). Slice fennel thinly; combine with celery and parsley in large bowl. Combine remaining ingredients in small bowl, pour over slaw mixture; toss gently to combine.

per serving 8.8g total fat (2.9g saturated fat); 1371kJ (328 cal); 21.2g carbohydrate; 40.8g protein; 4.9g fibre

prawn ravioli with mint and pea purée

preparation time 40 minutes
cooking time 15 minutes
serves 4

1¼ cups (310ml) chicken stock
2½ cups (300g)) frozen peas
½ cup loosely packed fresh mint leaves
40g butter
1 clove garlic, crushed
1kg uncooked medium king prawns
1 egg white
1 tablespoon sweet chilli sauce
2 tablespoons lemon juice
1 long green chilli, chopped finely
40 wonton wrappers
¼ cup (30g) frozen peas, extra

1 Bring chicken stock to a boil in medium pan. Add peas, mint and butter; return to a boil. Reduce heat; simmer, uncovered, about 5 minutes until peas are soft. Cool 10 minutes; blend with garlic until smooth.
2 Meanwhile, shell and devein prawns; chop half the prawns coarsely. Blend or process remaining whole prawns with egg white, sauce and half of the juice until mixture is almost smooth. Combine in large bowl with chopped prawn and chilli.
3 Centre 1 level tablespoon of prawn mixture on one wrapper; brush edges with water. Top with another wrapper; seal edges. Repeat with remaining prawn mixture and wrappers (makes 20 ravioli). Cook ravioli, in batches, in large uncovered pan of boiling water, until ravioli float to the surface and are cooked.
4 Meanwhile, return pea puree to same medium pan, add extra peas and remaining juice; stir over heat until peas are just tender.
5 Divide ravioli among plates; top with pea puree.

per serving 10.8g total fat (6g saturated fat); 1613kJ (386 cal); 34g carbohydrate; 37.3g protein; 6.7g fibre

pepper-crusted beef fillet with vegetable and polenta

preparation time 20 minutes (plus refrigeration time)
cooking time 1 hour 5 minutes
serves 4

3 cups (750ml) water
¾ cup (120g) polenta
2 tablespoons wholegrain mustard
2 teaspoons cracked black pepper
600g beef eye fillet
1 large sweet potato (500g)
2 large parsnips (700g)
2 large carrots (360g)
2 teaspoons olive oil
cooking-oil spray
½ cup coarsely chopped fresh flat-leaf parsley
¼ cup (60ml) balsamic vinegar
¼ cup (60ml) water, extra
1 tablespoon wholegrain mustard, extra
1 tablespoon honey

1 Lightly oil deep 23cm-square cake tin.
2 Bring the water to a boil in medium saucepan. Gradually add polenta to liquid, stirring constantly. Reduce heat; cook, stirring constantly, about 10 minutes or until polenta thickens. Stir in half of the mustard; spread polenta into prepared tin. Cover; refrigerate about 1 hour or until firm.
3 Preheat oven to moderately hot.
4 Spread combined remaining mustard and pepper all over beef. Cut peeled vegetables into similar-sized baton shapes. Place combined vegetables, in single layer, in large shallow flameproof baking dish; drizzle with oil. Roast, uncovered, in moderately hot oven 10 minutes. Add beef to dish; roast, uncovered, in moderately hot oven about 35 minutes or until vegetables are crisp and beef is cooked as desired.
5 Meanwhile, turn polenta onto board; cut into baton shapes similar to vegetables. Coat polenta with cooking-oil spray; place, in single layer, on oven tray. Place polenta in same oven with beef and vegetables for about the last 20 minutes of cooking time or until browned lightly.
6 Remove beef from baking dish. Cover beef; stand 5 minutes before slicing thinly. Place vegetables in large bowl with parsley; toss gently to combine. Cover to keep warm.
7 Place baking dish over high heat; add vinegar, the extra water, extra mustard and honey. Cook, stirring, about 5 minutes or until sauce bubbles and thickens. Serve vegetables, polenta and beef, drizzled with sauce.

per serving 11.1g total fat (3.3g saturated fat); 2140kJ (512 cal); 61.1g carbohydrate; 40.7g protein; 9.6g fibre

veal cutlets with onion marmalade

preparation time 15 minutes (plus refrigeration time)
cooking time 40 minutes
serves 4

2 teaspoons olive oil
1 clove garlic, crushed
1 teaspoon cracked black pepper
4 veal cutlets (680g)
20g butter
2 large red onions (600g), sliced thinly
⅓ cup (75g) firmly packed brown sugar
¼ cup (60ml) apple cider vinegar
2 tablespoons orange juice
2 teaspoons finely chopped fresh rosemary
2 cobs corn (800g), trimmed, cut into 3cm pieces
500g asparagus, trimmed

1 Combine oil, garlic and pepper in large bowl, add veal; toss veal to coat in marinade. Cover; refrigerate until required.
2 Meanwhile, heat butter in medium frying pan; cook onion, stirring, until soft and browned lightly. Add sugar, vinegar and juice; cook, stirring, about 15 minutes or until onion caramelises. Remove from heat; stir in rosemary.
3 Cook corn and asparagus, in batches, on heated oiled grill plate (or grill or barbecue) until browned lightly and cooked as desired; cover to keep warm.
4 Cook veal on same grill plate (or grill or barbecue) until cooked as desired. Serve veal, corn and asparagus topped with onion marmalade.

per serving 11.7g total fat (4.1g saturated fat); 1965kJ (470 cal); 50.8g carbohydrate; 40.1g protein; 10.4g fibre

herb-stuffed chicken with tomato salad

preparation time 25 minutes
cooking time 25 minutes
serves 4

¼ cup finely chopped fresh basil
1 tablespoon finely chopped fresh oregano
2 teaspoons fresh lemon thyme
2 cloves garlic, crushed
1 tablespoon finely grated lemon rind
4 chicken breast fillets (680g)
4 slices prosciutto (60g)
250g cherry tomatoes
250g yellow mini plum tomatoes
150g baby spinach leaves
½ cup coarsely chopped fresh basil
2 tablespoons red wine vinegar
2 teaspoons olive oil

1 Preheat oven to moderate.
2 Combine finely chopped basil, oregano, thyme, garlic and rind in small bowl. Using meat mallet, gently pound chicken, one at a time, between pieces of cling film until about 5mm thick. Divide herb mixture among chicken pieces; roll to enclose filling, wrapping each roll with prosciutto slice to secure.
3 Cook chicken in heated lightly oiled large frying pan, uncovered, about 10 minutes or until browned all over. Place chicken on baking tray; cook, uncovered, in preheated moderate oven about 15 minutes or until cooked through.
4 Meanwhile, cook tomatoes in same pan, over high heat, stirring, 3 minutes. Gently toss tomatoes, spinach and coarsely chopped basil in large bowl with combined vinegar and oil. Serve salad with chicken.

per serving 7.4g total fat (1.7g saturated fat); 1066kJ (255 cal); 3.4g carbohydrate; 42.9g protein; 3.6g fibre

chicken donburi

preparation time 20 minutes (plus standing time)
cooking time 40 minutes
serves 4

4 dried shiitake mushrooms
½ teaspoon dashi powder
1 cup (250ml) boiling water
4 medium brown onions (600g), sliced thinly
1½ cups (300g) koshihikari rice
3 cups (750ml) cold water
¼ cup (60ml) soy sauce
2 tablespoons mirin
1 teaspoon white sugar
600g chicken breast fillets, chopped coarsely
4 eggs, beaten lightly
2 spring onions, sliced thinly

1 Place mushrooms in small heatproof bowl, cover with boiling water, stand 20 minutes; drain. Discard stems; slice caps thinly.
2 Meanwhile, combine dashi with the boiling water in small jug.
3 Cook brown onion in heated lightly oiled large frying pan, stirring, about 10 minutes or until onion is browned lightly. Add half of the dashi mixture, reduce heat; simmer, stirring occasionally, about 10 minutes or until softened. Transfer to medium bowl.
4 Bring rice and the cold water to a boil in large saucepan, uncovered, stirring occasionally. Reduce heat to as low as possible; cover with a tight-fitting lid, cook rice 12 minutes. Do not remove lid or stir rice during cooking time. Remove from heat; stand, covered, 10 minutes.
5 Meanwhile, combine remaining dashi mixture with sauce, mirin and sugar in same frying pan; bring to a boil. Add chicken and mushroom; cook, covered, about 5 minutes or until chicken is cooked through.
6 Combine egg with cooked onion in bowl, pour over chicken mixture; cook, covered, over low heat, about 5 minutes or until egg just sets.
7 Divide rice among serving bowls; top with chicken mixture, sprinkle with spring onion.
TIP A Japanese culinary term, donburi is made with rice, vegetables and a single variety of any meat; it is also the name given to the dish in which this recipe is cooked. This version, oyako donburi, translates as parent and child, as it's made with both chicken and eggs.

per serving 9.4g total fat (2.7g saturated fat); 2328kJ (557 cal); 67.9g carbohydrate; 48.9g protein; 2.9g fibre

balsamic-seared steak with potatoes and mushrooms

preparation time 15 minutes (plus refrigeration time)
cooking time 15 minutes serves 4

¼ cup (60ml) balsamic vinegar
2 cloves garlic, crushed
4 beef scotch fillet steaks (800g)
1kg salad potatoes, quartered lengthways
1 tablespoon olive oil
500g flat mushrooms, sliced thickly
2 tablespoons dry red wine
1 tablespoon plum jam
1 tablespoon cornflour
¾ cup (180ml) beef stock

1 Combine vinegar and garlic in medium bowl, add beef; toss beef to coat in marinade. Cover; refrigerate 3 hours or overnight.
2 Preheat oven to moderately hot.
3 Place potato, in single layer, in large shallow baking tin; drizzle with oil. Roast, uncovered, in moderately hot oven, stirring occasionally, about 30 minutes or until browned lightly and crisp.
4 Meanwhile, cook steaks on heated lightly oiled grill plate (or grill or barbecue) until cooked as desired. Cover to keep warm.
5 Cook mushroom on same heated grill plate (or grill or barbecue) until just tender.
6 Place wine in small saucepan; bring to a boil. Add jam and blended cornflour and stock; stir until sauce boils and thickens slightly. Serve steaks with mushrooms, potato and sauce.

per serving 13.7g total fat (4.3g saturated fat); 2165kJ (518 cal); 40.8g carbohydrate; 54.2g protein; 8.4g fibre

glazed-chicken tortilla with sprout and herb salad

preparation time 15 minutes
cooking time 20 minutes
serves 4

¼ cup (80g) cranberry sauce
1 tablespoon wholegrain mustard
1 tablespoon lemon juice
5cm piece fresh ginger (25g), grated
1 clove garlic, crushed
500g chicken breast fillets
1 small red onion (100g), sliced thinly
60g mangetout sprouts
¼ cup thinly sliced fresh coriander
¼ cup thinly sliced fresh mint
1 tablespoon white wine vinegar
4 large flour tortillas

1 Heat combined sauce, mustard, juice, ginger and garlic in small saucepan, stirring, until glaze comes to a boil.
2 Cook chicken, in batches, in heated lightly oiled large frying pan, brushing frequently with glaze, until cooked through. Cover chicken; stand 5 minutes before slicing thickly.
3 Meanwhile, place onion, sprouts, herbs and vinegar in medium bowl; toss salad gently to combine. Heat tortillas according to manufacturer's instructions.
4 Divide chicken and salad among centres of tortillas; roll tortillas around filling to form cone shapes.

per serving 5.6g total fat (1.2g saturated fat); 1296kJ (310 cal); 31g carbohydrate; 33.4g protein; 2.9g fibre

grilled lamb cutlets with warm risoni salad

preparation time 15 minutes (plus refrigeration time)
cooking time 35 minutes
serves 4

1 clove garlic, crushed
1 tablespoon finely chopped fresh oregano
1 tablespoon finely chopped fresh chives
2 tablespoons lemon juice
¼ cup (60ml) dry white wine
12 french-trimmed lamb cutlets (700g)

WARM RISONI SALAD

500g pumpkin, diced into 3cm pieces
1 clove garlic, crushed
1 tablespoon olive oil
1 cup (220g) risoni
150g baby spinach leaves
2 tablespoons lemon juice
2 tablespoons coarsely chopped fresh chives
2 tablespoons fresh oregano leaves

1 Combine garlic, oregano, chives, juice and wine in large bowl, add lamb; toss lamb to coat in marinade. Cover; refrigerate until required.
2 Meanwhile, make warm risoni salad.
3 Drain lamb; discard marinade. Cook lamb, in batches, on heated lightly oiled grill plate (or grill or barbecue) until cooked as desired. Serve cutlets with salad.

WARM RISONI SALAD
Preheat oven to moderately hot. Place pumpkin, in single layer, on oven tray; drizzle with combined garlic and half of the oil. Roast, uncovered, in moderately hot oven about 15 minutes or until pumpkin is browned lightly and tender. Meanwhile, cook pasta in large saucepan of boiling water, uncovered, until just tender; drain. Combine pasta and spinach in large bowl with pumpkin, juice, herbs and remaining oil; toss gently to combine.
TIP Risoni is a small rice-shaped pasta; you can use any small soup pasta for this recipe.

per serving 11.5g total fat (3.6g saturated fat); 1735kJ (415 cal); 46.4g carbohydrate; 28g protein; 5.4g fibre

lamb and lentil curry

preparation time 15 minutes
cooking time 55 minutes
serves 4

1 cup (200g) yellow split peas
1 tablespoon olive oil
600g lamb fillets, diced into 4cm pieces
2 large brown onions (400g), sliced thinly
5cm piece fresh ginger (25g), chopped finely
2 cloves garlic, crushed
2 tablespoons ground coriander
1 tablespoon sweet paprika
½ teaspoon cayenne pepper
200g plain yogurt
2 medium tomatoes (300g), chopped coarsely
1¾ cups (430ml) chicken stock
⅔ cup (160ml) light coconut cream
150g baby spinach leaves
⅓ cup coarsely chopped fresh coriander

1 Cook split peas in medium saucepan of boiling water, uncovered, until just tender; drain.
2 Meanwhile, heat half of the oil in large saucepan; cook lamb, in batches, stirring, until cooked as desired. Drain on absorbent paper.
3 Heat remaining oil in same pan; cook onion, stirring, about 15 minutes or until caramelised. Add ginger, garlic, ground coriander, paprika and cayenne; cook, stirring, until fragrant. Add yogurt; cook 5 minutes, without boiling, stirring occasionally.
4 Add tomato, stock and coconut cream; bring to a boil. Reduce heat; simmer, uncovered, about 15 minutes or until sauce thickens slightly.
5 Return lamb to pan with split peas and spinach; cook, stirring, until heated through. Remove from heat; stir in fresh coriander.

per serving 19.3g total fat (9.8g saturated fat); 2153kJ (515 cal); 33.5g carbohydrate; 51.7g protein; 8.9g fibre

squid stuffed with smoked trout and basil

preparation time 20 minutes
cooking time 10 minutes
serves 4

1 small red onion (100g)
300g hot-smoked ocean trout fillets, flaked coarsely
1 cup coarsely chopped fresh basil
8 baby squid hoods (500g), cleaned
100g baby rocket leaves
½ cup loosely packed fresh flat-leaf parsley leaves
1 cup coarsely chopped fresh mint
¼ cup (60ml) white wine vinegar
1 tablespoon olive oil
2 limes, cut into 8 wedges

1 Slice half the onion thinly; chop remaining half finely.
2 Combine chopped onion, fish and half of the basil in small bowl; fill hoods with fish mixture up to about 2cm from opening, secure with toothpicks.
3 Cook squid in heated lightly oiled large frying pan, uncovered, until browned lightly all over and tender.
4 Place rocket, parsley, mint, sliced onion and remaining basil in large bowl with combined vinegar and oil; toss gently to combine.
5 Cut squid in half on the diagonal; divide pieces among plates with salad and lime wedges.

per serving   10.3g total fat (2.1g saturated fat); 1158kJ (277 cal); 2.6g carbohydrate; 41.7g protein; 3g fibre

grilled snapper with spicy tomato sauce

preparation time 15 minutes
cooking time 15 minutes
serves 4

2 tablespoons olive oil
3 cloves garlic, crushed
3 shallots (75g), chopped finely
425g can diced tomatoes
1 tablespoon dry sherry
1 tablespoon soy sauce
1 teaspoon sambal oelek
2 teaspoons white sugar
4 snapper fillets (800g)
75g baby spinach leaves
2 teaspoons red wine vinegar

1 Heat half of the oil in small frying pan; cook garlic and shallots, stirring, about 1 minute or until shallots soften. Stir in undrained tomatoes, sherry, sauce, sambal and sugar; bring to a boil. Reduce heat; simmer, uncovered, about 10 minutes or until liquid has reduced by half.
2 Meanwhile, cook fish, uncovered, in heated lightly oiled large frying pan about 10 minutes or until cooked as desired.
3 Place spinach in medium bowl with combined vinegar and remaining oil; toss gently to combine. Serve fish with spicy sauce and spinach salad.

per serving   12.7g total fat (2.5g saturated fat); 1325kJ (317 cal); 6.3g carbohydrate; 42.5g protein; 2.3g fibre

ocean trout in baby pak choy parcels

preparation time 20 minutes (plus standing time)
cooking time 15 minutes
serves 4

4 dried shiitake mushrooms
2 spring onions, chopped finely
3cm piece fresh ginger (15g), grated
5cm stick (10g) finely chopped fresh lemongrass
2 cloves garlic, crushed
1 teaspoon sambal oelek
2 tablespoons soy sauce
4 ocean trout fillets (600g)
4 large baby pak choy (600g)
1½ cups (300g) jasmine rice
GINGER DRESSING
2cm piece fresh ginger (10g), grated
2 tablespoons rice wine vinegar
1 tablespoon vegetable oil
1 teaspoon sesame oil
2 tablespoons mirin
1 tablespoon soy sauce

1 Place mushrooms in small heatproof bowl, cover with boiling water, stand 20 minutes; drain. Discard stems; chop caps finely.
2 Meanwhile, combine ginger dressing ingredients in screw-top jar; shake well.
3 Combine mushroom, onion, ginger, lemongrass, garlic, sambal and sauce in small bowl; divide mushroom mixture among flesh side of fish fillets. Carefully insert one fillet, mushroom-side up, inside leaves of each pak choy; wrap leaves around fillet then tie parcels with kitchen string.
4 Place parcels in large steamer fitted over large saucepan of boiling water; steam, covered, about 10 minutes or until fish is cooked as desired.
5 Meanwhile, cook rice in large saucepan of boiling water, uncovered, until rice is just tender; drain. Divide rice among plates; top with parcels, drizzle with dressing.
TIP Wash the pak choy carefully. It's important to remove all the dirt hidden among the leaves without actually separating any of the leaves from the base, thus leaving each vegetable intact.

per serving 12.3g total fat (2.2g saturated fat); 2195kJ (525 cal); 64.6g carbohydrate; 37.1g protein; 3.6g fibre

moroccan fish kebabs with almond and lemon couscous

preparation time 25 minutes (plus refrigeration time)
cooking time 10 minutes
serves 4

½ cup finely chopped fresh coriander
2 cloves garlic, crushed
2 tablespoons olive oil
2 fresh small red thai chillies, chopped finely
¼ cup (60ml) lemon juice
800g skinless white fish fillets, diced into
3cm pieces
1½ cups (375ml) chicken stock
1½ cups (300g) couscous
½ cup firmly packed fresh coriander leaves
1 tablespoon finely chopped preserved lemon
¼ cup (35g) toasted slivered almonds

1 Combine chopped coriander, garlic, oil, chilli and juice in small bowl. Place half of the coriander mixture in large bowl, add fish; toss fish to coat in mixture. Thread fish onto skewers; place kebabs on tray. Cover; refrigerate 45 minutes.
2 Cook kebabs on heated lightly oiled grill plate (or grill or barbecue) about 5 minutes or until cooked as desired.
3 Meanwhile, bring stock to a boil in small saucepan; remove from heat. Add couscous to stock, cover; stand about 5 minutes or until liquid is absorbed, fluffing with fork occasionally. Add remaining coriander mixture, coriander leaves, lemon and nuts; toss gently to combine. Serve couscous with kebabs.
TIP You will need to soak eight 25cm bamboo skewers in water for at least an hour before using to prevent them from splintering or scorching.

per serving 16g total fat (2.2g saturated fat); 2391kJ (572 cal); 59.2g carbohydrate; 46.6 protein; 2.6g fibre

asian-spiced salmon with nashi, mint and coriander salad

preparation time 20 minutes
cooking time 20 minutes
serves 4

2 teaspoons sichuan peppercorns, crushed
2 star anise
1 tablespoon soy sauce
2 tablespoons honey
cooking-oil spray
4 salmon fillets (800g)
2 medium nashi pears (400g), sliced thinly
1 fresh long red chilli, sliced thinly
1 medium red onion (170g), sliced thinly
2 spring onions, sliced thinly
¾ cup loosely packed fresh mint leaves
¾ cup loosely packed fresh coriander leaves
SESAME SOY DRESSING
2 tablespoons soy sauce
¼ cup (60ml) mirin
2 teaspoons caster sugar
¼ teaspoon sesame oil

1 Preheat oven to moderate.
2 Dry-fry spices in small frying pan until fragrant. Add sauce and honey; bring to a boil. Reduce heat; simmer, uncovered, 2 minutes.
3 Line large shallow baking dish with foil, extending foil 5cm above long sides of dish; coat lightly with cooking-oil spray. Place fish on foil; brush both sides with spice mixture. Bake, uncovered, in moderate oven about 15 minutes or until cooked as desired.
4 Meanwhile, place sesame soy dressing ingredients in screw-top jar; shake well.
5 Place remaining ingredients in large bowl, add dressing; toss gently to combine. Serve salad with fish.
TIP If nashi pears are not available, substitute with crisp green apples.

per serving 17.5g total fat (3.7g saturated fat); 1864kJ (446 cal); 26.7g carbohydrate; 45.5g protein; 4g fibre

sumac, salt and pepper fish with mediterranean salad

preparation time 20 minutes
cooking time 10 minutes
serves 4

2 tablespoons sumac
1 teaspoon salt
1 teaspoon cracked black pepper
4 firm white fillets (800g)
1 cup (200g) couscous
1 cup (250ml) boiling water
1 tablespoon olive oil
1 lemon, quartered

MEDITERRANEAN SALAD
2 medium tomatoes (300g), deseeded,
chopped coarsely
2 medium red peppers (400g), chopped coarsely
2 tablespoons pitted kalamata olives,
chopped coarsely
2 tablespoons drained baby capers, rinsed
1 cup coarsely chopped fresh flat-leaf parsley

1 Combine sumac, salt and pepper in large bowl,
add fish; turn fish to coat in mixture. Cook fish, in
batches, in heated lightly oiled large frying pan until
cooked as desired.
2 Meanwhile, place mediterranean salad ingredients
in medium bowl; toss gently to combine.
3 Combine couscous with the water in large heatproof
bowl. Cover; stand about 5 minutes or until water is
absorbed, fluffing with fork occasionally. Stir in oil.
4 Divide couscous among plates, top with salad and
fish; serve with lemon.
*TIP You can use any firm white-fleshed fish fillets for
this recipe.*

*per serving 9.7g total fat (2.1g saturated fat); 1990kJ
(476 cal); 45.7g carbohydrate; 49.9g protein; 3.9g fibre*

thai-flavoured mussels

preparation time 30 minutes
cooking time 10 minutes
serves 4

2kg large black mussels
2 tablespoons water
⅓ cup (80ml) lime juice
2 tablespoons grated palm sugar
2 tablespoons fish sauce
1 fresh long red chilli, chopped finely
2 teaspoons groundnut oil
10cm stick (20g) finely chopped fresh lemongrass
1 clove garlic, crushed
4cm piece fresh ginger (20g), grated
2 teaspoons finely chopped coriander roots
and stems
2 spring onions, sliced thinly
½ cup firmly packed fresh coriander leaves
½ cup firmly packed fresh thai basil leaves
2 fresh long red chillies, sliced thinly

1 Scrub mussels under cold water; discard beards.
2 Whisk the water, juice, sugar, sauce and chopped chilli in small jug.
3 Heat oil in large saucepan; cook lemongrass, garlic, ginger and coriander roots and stems, stirring, until fragrant. Stir in lime mixture; bring to a boil. Add mussels; return to a boil. Reduce heat; simmer, covered, about 5 minutes or until mussels open (discard any that do not).
4 Divide mussels and cooking liquid among plates; sprinkle with onion, coriander leaves, basil and sliced chilli.
TIP When removing the leaves from a bunch of coriander, remove some of the stems and roots for this recipe.

per serving 4.2g total fat (0.9g saturated fat); 594kJ (142 cal); 12.5g carbohydrate; 13.1g protein; 0.9g fibre

seared tuna with chilled soba

preparation time 15 minutes (plus refrigeration time)
cooking time 5 minutes
serves 4

200g dried soba noodles
¼ cup (60ml) mirin
2 tablespoons kecap manis
1 tablespoon cooking sake
2 teaspoons white sugar
5cm piece fresh ginger (25g), grated
1 clove garlic, crushed
4 tuna steaks (800g)
1 sheet toasted seaweed (yaki-nori), sliced thinly
2 spring onions, chopped finely
1 teaspoon sesame oil
2 tablespoons pickled ginger, sliced thinly

1 Cook soba noodles in large saucepan of boiling water, uncovered, until just tender; drain. Rinse under cold water; drain. Place in medium bowl, cover; refrigerate until required.
2 Meanwhile, combine mirin, kecap manis, sake, sugar, fresh ginger and garlic in small jug.
3 Cook fish in heated lightly oiled large frying pan, uncovered, until cooked as desired (tuna can become very dry if overcooked; we recommend you sear it over very high heat for about 30 seconds each side). Add mirin mixture to pan; coat fish both sides in mixture. Remove fish from pan; cover to keep warm.
4 Bring mixture in pan to a boil. Reduce heat; simmer, uncovered, 30 seconds. Strain sauce into small jug.
5 Meanwhile, place seaweed, onion, oil and pickled ginger in bowl with soba; toss gently to combine. Divide fish among plates, drizzle with sauce; top with soba. Serve with wasabi, if desired.

per serving 13.2g total fat (4.9g saturated fat); 2182kJ (522 cal); 41.9g carbohydrate; 56.3g protein; 2.6g fibre

desserts and cakes

brown-sugar meringues with banana and caramel sauce

preparation time 15 minutes
cooking time 1 hour
serves 4

3 egg whites
¾ cup (165g) firmly packed dark brown sugar
3 teaspoons cornflour
3 teaspoons white vinegar
1 teaspoon vanilla extract
10g butter
⅓ cup (80ml) single cream
¼ cup (55g) firmly packed dark brown sugar, extra
2 medium bananas (400g), sliced thinly

1 Preheat oven to very low.
2 Beat egg whites in small bowl with electric mixer until soft peaks form. Gradually add sugar, 1 tablespoon at a time, beating until sugar dissolves between additions; fold in cornflour, vinegar and extract.
3 Divide meringue mixture among four shallow ¾-cup (180ml) ovenproof dishes. Place dishes on oven tray; bake, uncovered, in very low oven about 1 hour or until meringues are firm.
4 Meanwhile, melt butter in small saucepan, add cream and extra sugar; bring to a boil. Reduce heat; simmer, uncovered, about 2 minutes or until mixture thickens slightly.
5 Divide banana slices among meringues; drizzle with caramel sauce.

per serving 7.5g total fat (4.9g saturated fat); 1463kJ (350 cal); 69.1g carbohydrate; 4.5g protein; 1.5g fibre

summer berry stack

preparation time 20 minutes
cooking time 5 minutes
serves 4

450g brioche loaf
250g strawberries, sliced thickly
150g raspberries
150g blueberries
1 tablespoon icing sugar

BLACKBERRY COULIS
300g frozen blackberries
¼ cup (40g) icing sugar
¼ cup (60ml) water

1 Make blackberry coulis.
2 Using 7cm cutter, cut twelve 1cm-thick slices from brioche loaf; cut one round from each slice.
3 Combine berries in medium bowl.
4 Place one round on each plate; divide a third of the berries among rounds. Place another round on top of each stack; divide half of the remaining berries among stacks. Place remaining rounds on berry stacks; top with remaining berries.
5 Pour coulis over stacks; dust each stack with sifted icing sugar.

BLACKBERRY COULIS
Stir ingredients in medium pan over high heat; bring to a boil. Reduce heat; simmer, uncovered, 3 minutes. Strain coulis into medium jug; cool 10 minutes.
TIP Toast any leftover brioche loaf for breakfast, or use it to make a bread and butter pudding.

per serving 7.2g total fat (3g saturated fat); 1313kJ (314 cal); 55.3g carbohydrate; 7.5g protein; 9.7g fibre

pavlova roll with banana, kiwi and passionfruit

preparation time 25 minutes
cooking time 20 minutes
serves 10

4 egg whites
¾ cup (165g) caster sugar
1 teaspoon cornflour
1 teaspoon white vinegar
1 teaspoon vanilla extract
1 tablespoon icing sugar
300ml thickened single cream
1 large banana (230g), halved lengthways, sliced thinly
2 medium kiwi fruit (170g), quartered lengthways
⅓ cup (80ml) passionfruit pulp (approximately 4 passionfruit)

1 Preheat oven to moderately low. Grease 25cm x 30cm swiss roll tin; line base with baking parchment, extending paper 5cm over long sides of tin.
2 Beat egg whites in small bowl with electric mixer until soft peaks form. Gradually add caster sugar, 1 tablespoon at a time, beating until sugar dissolves between additions; fold in cornflour, vinegar and extract. Spread meringue mixture into prepared tin; bake, uncovered, in moderately low oven about 20 minutes or until browned lightly.
3 Turn meringue onto sheet of baking parchment sprinkled with half of the sifted icing sugar; remove lining paper, trim short ends of meringue.
4 Beat cream and remaining sifted icing sugar in small bowl with electric mixer until soft peaks form. Spread cream mixture over slightly warm meringue; place fruit lengthways along centre of meringue. Roll meringue firmly from long side, using paper as a guide. Refrigerate until ready to serve.

per serving 8.1g total fat (5.3g saturated fat); 748kJ (179 cal); 24.6g carbohydrate; 3g protein; 1.9g fibre

frozen passionfruit yogurt

preparation time 10 minutes (plus freezing time)
cooking time 5 minutes serves 4

½ cup (110g) caster sugar
¼ cup (60ml) water
1 teaspoon gelatine
2 cups (560g) low-fat yogurt
½ cup (125ml) passionfruit pulp

1 Combine sugar and the water in small pan, stirring over low heat until sugar dissolves; transfer to jug.
2 Sprinkle gelatine over sugar syrup, stirring until gelatine dissolves.
3 Combine yogurt and pulp in jug with syrup. Pour yogurt mixture into loaf pan, cover tightly with foil; freeze 3 hours or until almost set. Scrape yogurt from bottom and sides of pan with fork; return to freezer until firm.
TIP You need approximately six passionfruit for this recipe.

per serving 2.5g total fat (1.5g saturated fat); 924kJ (221 cal); 39.9g carbohydrate; 8.6g protein; 4.3g fibre

caramelised figs with spiced yogurt

preparation time 10 minutes
cooking time 10 minutes serves 4

1 cup (280g) low-fat yogurt
¼ cup (35g) toasted pistachios, chopped coarsely
¼ teaspoon ground nutmeg
1 tablespoon caster sugar
6 large fresh figs (480g)
1 tablespoon honey

1 Combine yogurt, nuts, nutmeg and sugar in bowl.
2 Halve figs lengthways. Brush cut-side with honey.
3 Cook figs, cut-side down, uncovered, in heated large non-stick frying pan 5 minutes. Turn figs; cook, uncovered, 5 minutes or until browned lightly. Serve figs with spiced yogurt.

per serving 6g total fat (1.3g saturated fat); 777kJ (186 cal); 26.1g carbohydrate; 6.8g protein; 3.6g fibre

rice pudding with raspberries

preparation time 10 minutes
cooking time 1 hour 20 minutes serves 4

½ cup (100g) white short-grain rice
3 cups (750ml) semi-skimmed milk
1 teaspoon vanilla extract
¼ cup (55g) caster sugar
RASPBERRY COMPOTE
300g frozen raspberries
1 tablespoon caster sugar

1 Preheat oven to moderately low. Rinse rice under cold water; drain. Spread in shallow 1-litre baking dish.
2 Combine milk, extract and sugar in pan; bring to a boil. Pour over rice; mix gently with fork. Cover tightly with foil; bake about 1 hour 15 minutes until rice is softened and almost all liquid absorbed.
3 Meanwhile, combine compote ingredients in small saucepan; stir over low heat until sugar dissolves. Cool 10 minutes. Serve compote with pudding.

per serving 5.4g total fat (3.3g saturated fat); 1237kJ (296 cal); 52.1g carbohydrate; 9.6g protein; 4.3g fibre

cherry cheesecake parfaits

preparation time 15 minutes (plus refrigeration time)
cooking time 10 minutes serves 4

1 tablespoon caster sugar
1 tablespoon kirsch
425g can pitted black cherries, undrained
2 teaspoons cornflour blended with 1 tablespoon water
60g low-fat cream cheese
200g low-fat cheesecake yogurt
4 sponge finger biscuits (50g), halved

1 Stir sugar, kirsch and cherries in small pan over low heat until sugar dissolves; bring to a boil. Remove from heat; reserve ⅔ cup liquid. Return pan to heat, add cornflour and water; cook, stirring, until mixture boils and thickens slightly. Remove from heat; cool 10 minutes.
2 Beat cream cheese with yogurt.
3 Dip biscuits in reserved liquid. Divide among four serving glasses; top with cherry mixture then cream-cheese mixture. Refrigerate parfaits, covered, 30 minutes before serving.

per serving 4g total fat (2.4g saturated fat); 790kJ (189 cal); 32.3g carbohydrate; 5.3g protein; 1g fibre

tropical fruit sorbets

preparation time 20 minutes (plus freezing time)
cooking time 10 minutes
serves 4

½ cup (125ml) water
½ cup (110g) caster sugar
2 egg whites

*The basic sorbet mixture makes four servings;
use only one of the three different fruit flavours given
below for that amount of sorbet. However, if you wish,
you can make all three flavours by tripling the basic
sorbet recipe.*

1 Stir the water and sugar in small saucepan over
heat until sugar dissolves; bring to a boil. Reduce heat;
simmer, uncovered, without stirring, 5 minutes. Transfer
to large heatproof jug, cool 10 minutes.
2 Meanwhile, blend or process fruit of your choice
(see recipes below) until pureed. You need 2 cups of
fruit puree for this recipe; freeze any that is left over.
Stir puree into sugar syrup.
3 Pour sorbet mixture into loaf tin, cover tightly with foil;
freeze 3 hours or overnight.
4 Blend or process mixture with egg whites until
smooth. Return to loaf tin, cover; freeze until firm.

PINEAPPLE
Blend or process 1 small peeled and coarsely chopped
pineapple (900g) then follow the basic sorbet recipe in
Step 2 above.

*per serving 0.1g total fat (0g saturated fat); 656kJ
(157 cal); 36.9g carbohydrate; 3g protein; 2.5g fibre*

KIWI FRUIT
Blend or process 7 medium peeled kiwi fruit (600g) then
follow the basic sorbet recipe in Step 2 above.

*per serving 0.3g total fat (0g saturated fat); 732kJ
(175 cal); 40.1g carbohydrate; 3.6g protein; 4.2g fibre*

MANGO
 Blend or process 3 small peeled and pitted mangoes
(900g) then follow the basic sorbet recipe in Step 2
above.

*per serving 0.3g total fat (0g saturated fat); 849kJ
(203 cal); 47.7g carbohydrate; 3.4g protein; 2.4g fibre*

spiced stone-fruit strudel

preparation time 20 minutes
cooking time 25 minutes
serves 4

2 medium peaches (300g), quartered, sliced thinly
2 medium nectarines (340g), quartered, sliced thinly
2 tablespoons brown sugar
½ cup (80g) sultanas
1½ teaspoons ground cinnamon
½ teaspoon ground nutmeg
⅓ cup (25g) fresh breadcrumbs
6 sheets filo pastry
20g butter, melted
2 tablespoons milk
2 teaspoons icing sugar

1 Combine peach, nectarine, brown sugar, sultanas, spices and breadcrumbs in medium bowl.
2 Preheat oven to moderately hot. Grease oven tray and line with baking parchment.
3 Stack filo sheets, brushing each lightly with half the combined butter and milk. Cut filo stack in half widthways; cover one stack with baking parchment, then with a damp tea towel, to prevent drying out.
4 Place half the fruit mixture along centre of filo stack; roll from one side to enclose filling, sealing ends of roll with a little of the remaining butter mixture. Place strudel, seam-side down, on prepared tray; brush all over with a little of the remaining butter mixture. Repeat process with remaining filo stack, fruit mixture and butter mixture.
5 Bake strudels, uncovered, in moderately hot oven about 25 minutes or until browned lightly. Cut each strudel in half widthways; divide among plates, dust with sifted icing sugar.

per serving 5.5g total fat (3.1g saturated fat); 1191kJ (285 cal); 53.1g carbohydrate; 5.9g protein; 4.2g fibre

chocolate fudge cakes with coffee syrup

preparation time 15 minutes
cooking time 20 minutes
makes 12

½ cup (50g) cocoa powder
1 cup (220g) firmly packed brown sugar
½ cup (125ml) boiling water
85g dark cooking chocolate, chopped finely
2 egg yolks
¼ cup (30g) ground almonds
⅓ cup (50g) wholemeal plain flour
4 egg whites

COFFEE SYRUP
¾ cup (165g) firmly packed brown sugar
¾ cup (180ml) water
1 tablespoon instant coffee powder

1 Preheat oven to moderately low. Lightly grease 12-hole (⅓-cup/80ml) muffin tray.
2 Combine sifted cocoa and sugar in large bowl; blend in the water then chocolate, stir until smooth. Stir in egg yolks, ground almonds and flour.
3 Beat egg whites in small bowl with electric mixer until soft peaks form. Fold egg whites into chocolate mixture, in two batches; divide mixture among prepared holes of muffin tray. Bake, uncovered, in moderately low oven about 20 minutes.
4 Meanwhile, make coffee syrup.
5 Stand cakes in tray 5 minutes, divide among plates; drizzle hot cakes with hot coffee syrup.

COFFEE SYRUP
Stir sugar and the water in small saucepan over low heat until sugar dissolves; bring to a boil. Reduce heat; simmer, uncovered, without stirring, about 15 minutes or until syrup thickens. Stir in coffee; strain into small heatproof jug.

per cake 5.1g total fat (2g saturated fat); 895kJ (214 cal); 39.5g carbohydrate; 4.2g protein; 1.2g fibre

307

banana muffins with crunchy topping

preparation time 20 minutes
cooking time 20 minutes
makes 12

1¾ cups (280g) wholemeal self-raising flour
¾ cup (165g) firmly packed brown sugar
1 cup mashed banana
1 egg, beaten lightly
1 cup (250ml) buttermilk
¼ cup (60ml) vegetable oil

CRUNCHY OAT TOPPING
1 cup (90g) rolled oats
½ teaspoon ground nutmeg
2 tablespoons honey

1 Preheat oven to moderately hot. Lightly grease 12-hole (⅓-cup/80ml) muffin tray.
2 Make crunchy oat topping.
3 Sift flour and sugar into large bowl; stir in banana, egg, buttermilk and oil. Divide mixture among prepared holes of muffin tray; sprinkle with topping. Bake, uncovered, in moderately hot oven about 20 minutes. Stand muffins in tray 5 minutes; turn onto wire rack to cool.

CRUNCHY OAT TOPPING
Blend or process oats until coarsely chopped. Combine oats, nutmeg and honey in small bowl.
TIP You need approximately two large (460g) overripe bananas for this recipe.

per muffin 6.6g total fat (1.2g saturated fat); 1041kJ (249 cal); 42.5g carbohydrate; 5.6g protein; 3.7g fibre

blueberry scones with vanilla fromage frais

preparation time 10 minutes
cooking time 20 minutes
makes 8

2 cups (300g) self-raising flour
2 tablespoons icing sugar
1¼ cups (310ml) buttermilk
150g blueberries
200g light vanilla fromage frais

1 Preheat oven to hot. Grease shallow 20cm-round sandwich tin.
2 Sift flour and icing sugar into large bowl; pour in enough buttermilk to mix to a sticky dough. Fold in blueberries.
3 Gently knead dough on lightly floured surface until smooth; use hand to flatten out dough to about a 3cm thickness. Cut eight 5.5cm rounds from dough; place rounds, slightly touching, in prepared tin. Bake, uncovered, in hot oven about 20 minutes or until browned lightly; turn scones onto wire rack. Serve with fromage frais.
TIP To prevent dough from sticking, dust the inside of the cutter with flour.

per scone 2.6g total fat (1.5g saturated fat); 832kJ (199 cal); 36.2g carbohydrate; 7.1g protein; 1.8g fibre

chocolate rum and raisin loaf

preparation time 30 minutes (plus standing time)
cooking time 45 minutes
serves 12

¾ cup (125g) raisins, chopped finely
¼ cup (60ml) dark rum
½ cup (110g) caster sugar
1 egg
1 teaspoon vanilla extract
2 tablespoons golden syrup
80g butter, melted
¾ cup (180ml) buttermilk
1 cup (150g) self-raising flour
2 tablespoons cocoa powder
¼ teaspoon ground nutmeg
⅓ cup (65g) dark chocolate chips,
chopped coarsely

1 Preheat oven to moderate. Lightly grease 14cm x 21cm loaf tin; line base and two long sides with baking parchment, extending paper 5cm above edges of tin.
2 Combine raisins and rum in small bowl; stand, covered, 2 hours.
3 Beat sugar, egg, extract and syrup in small bowl with electric mixer until thick and creamy.
4 Transfer mixture to medium bowl; stir in butter, buttermilk and sifted flour, cocoa and nutmeg. Stir in undrained raisin mixture and chocolate chips.
5 Spread mixture into prepared tin; bake, uncovered, in moderate oven about 45 minutes. Stand 10 minutes; turn onto wire rack to cool.

per serving 7.7g total fat (4.9g saturated fat); 932kJ (223 cal); 33.6g carbohydrate; 3.2g protein; 1.1g fibre

cranberry, apricot and currant rock cakes

preparation time 15 minutes
cooking time 15 minutes
makes 20

2 cups (300g) self-raising flour
¼ teaspoon ground cinnamon
90g cold butter, chopped
⅓ cup (75g) caster sugar
½ cup (75g) currants
½ cup (75g) dried apricots, chopped coarsely
½ cup (75g) dried cranberries
1 egg, beaten lightly
½ cup (125ml) milk, approximately
1 tablespoon raw sugar

1 Preheat oven to moderately hot. Lightly grease two oven trays.
2 Combine flour and cinnamon in large bowl; rub in butter. Stir in caster sugar, fruit, egg and enough milk to give a moist but still firm consistency.
3 Drop rounded tablespoons of mixture about 5cm apart on prepared trays; sprinkle with raw sugar. Bake, uncovered, in moderately hot oven about 15 minutes or until browned lightly. Loosen cakes; cool on trays.

per cake 4.2g total fat (2.6g saturated fat); 564kJ (135 cal); 22.4g carbohydrate; 2.4g protein; 1.3g fibre

date and apple muesli slice

preparation time 15 minutes
cooking time 35 minutes
makes 32

2 medium apples (300g), grated coarsely
2 tablespoons lemon juice
¼ cup (60ml) water
50g butter
2 cups (340g) pitted dates
2 cups (220g) natural muesli
1 cup (220g) firmly packed brown sugar
1 cup (150g) plain flour
1 teaspoon ground cinnamon

1 Preheat oven to moderate. Lightly grease 25cm x 30cm swiss roll tin.
2 Combine apple, juice, the water, butter and dates in medium saucepan; bring to a boil. Reduce heat; simmer, covered, about 5 minutes or until apple is soft. Uncover; cook, stirring occasionally, about 5 minutes or until mixture thickens to a paste-like consistency.
3 Meanwhile, place muesli in large frying pan; stir over low heat about 5 minutes or until browned lightly. Combine muesli in large bowl with sugar, flour and cinnamon. Stir in date mixture.
4 Spread slice mixture into prepared tin; bake, uncovered, in moderate oven about 20 minutes or until firm. Cool in tin before cutting.

per slice 1.6g total fat (1g saturated fat); 326kJ (79 cal); 15.6g carbohydrate; 1g protein; 1g fibre

almond macaroons

preparation time 30 minutes
cooking time 10 minutes
makes 28

1 egg white
⅔ cup (150g) caster sugar
¼ teaspoon almond extract
1 cup (125g) ground almonds
½ cup (70g) toasted slivered almonds, chopped coarsely
50g dark chocolate, melted

1 Preheat oven to moderate. Lightly grease and line two oven trays.
2 Beat egg white in small bowl with electric mixer until soft peaks form. Gradually add sugar, 1 tablespoon at a time, beating until sugar dissolves between additions. Transfer egg-white mixture to medium bowl; fold in extract, ground almonds and nuts.
3 Divide mixture in half; roll each half into 20cm log. Cut each log into 14 pieces; roll each piece into 6cm log. Place logs on prepared trays; bake, uncovered, in moderate oven about 8 minutes. Cool on trays; drizzle or pipe macaroons with melted chocolate.

per macaroon 4.3g total fat (0.6g saturated fat); 297kJ (71 cal); 6.8g carbohydrate; 1.6g protein; 0.6g fibre

glossary

ALL-BRAN a low-fat, high-fibre bran-based breakfast cereal.

ALLSPICE also known as pimento or jamaican pepper; so-named because is tastes like a combination of nutmeg, cumin, clove and cinnamon – all spices.

ALMONDS

blanched skins removed.

essence often interchangeable with extract; made with almond oil and alcohol or another agent.

flaked paper-thin slices.

ground also known as almond meal; nuts are powdered to a coarse flour texture.

slivered cut lengthways.

AUBERGINE also known as eggplant; ranges in size from tiny to very large and in colour from pale green to deep purple.

BAKING POWDER a raising agent consisting mainly of two parts cream of tartar to one part bicarbonate of soda (baking soda). The acid and alkaline combination, when moistened and heated, gives off carbon dioxide which aerates and lightens the mixture during baking.

BAMBOO SHOOTS the tender shoots of bamboo plants, available in cans; must be drained and rinsed before use.

BARLEY a nutritious grain used in soups and stews. Hulled barley is the least processed form of barley and is high in fibre. Pearl barley has had the husk discarded and been hulled and polished, much the same as rice.

BARLEY FLAKES also known as rolled barley, and steamed and rolled barley; flattened grains produced by steaming the barley grain then rolling it into flakes. Used as a thickener in

soups and stews; also used to make porridges and muesli, and toppings for crumbles.

BAY LEAVES aromatic leaves from the bay tree used to flavour soups, stocks and casseroles.

BEANS

black-eyed also known as black-eyed peas.

borlotti also known as roman beans; can be eaten fresh or dried.

cannellini small, dried white bean similar in both appearance and flavour to other *Phaseolus vulgaris* varieties such as great northern, navy or haricot beans. Sometimes sold as butter beans.

GREEN sometimes called french or string beans, this long fresh bean is consumed pod and all.

YELLOW STRING also known as wax, french and runner; a yellow-coloured fresh green bean.

BEANSPROUTS also known as bean shoots; tender new growths of beans and seeds especially germinated for consumption as sprouts.

BEEF

eye fillet tenderloin; good for roasting and barbecuing.

mince also known as ground beef.

rump steak boneless tender cut, rib eye, sirloin and fillet steak are all suitable substitutes.

BEETROOT also known as red beets or just beets; firm, round root vegetable. Can be eaten raw, grated, in salads; boiled and sliced; or roasted then mashed like potatoes.

BICARBONATE OF SODA also known as baking soda.

BISCUITS also known as cookies.

nice an uniced, plain sweet biscuit

topped with a sprinkle of sugar; good for making the crust for cheesecakes.

sweet any plain sweet biscuit (or cookie) can be used as long as they are neither filled nor iced.

BLACK MUSTARD SEEDS also known as brown mustard seeds; more pungent than the white (or yellow) seeds used in most prepared mustards.

BREADCRUMBS

packaged fine-textured, crunchy, purchased, white breadcrumbs.

stale one- or two-day-old bread made into crumbs by grating, blending or processing.

BRIOCHE rich, French yeast-risen bread made with butter and eggs. Available from pâtisseries and most supermarkets.

BUCKWHEAT a herb in the same plant family as rhubarb; not a cereal so is gluten free. Available as flour (used to make blinis and soba noodles), coarsely ground, or whole and hulled (groats). Kasha, roasted buckwheat groats, is cooked like rice and has a nutty toasty flavour.

BULGHUR WHEAT also known as burghul. Hulled steamed wheat kernels that, once dried, are crushed into various-sized grains; not the same as cracked wheat. Used in Middle-Eastern dishes such as kibbeh and tabbouleh.

BUTTERMILK sold alongside fresh milk products in supermarkets; despite the implication of its name, is low in fat. Commercially made, by a method similar to yogurt. A good low-fat substitution for dairy products such as cream or soured cream; good in baking, sauces and salad dressings.

CARDAMOM native to India and used extensively in its cuisine; it can be purchased in pod, seed or ground form. Has a distinctive aromatic, sweetly rich flavour and is one of the world's most expensive spices.

CAYENNE PEPPER long, thin-fleshed, extremely hot, dried red chilli, usually purchased ground; both arbol and guajillo chillies are the fresh sources for cayenne.

CELERIAC also known as celery root or celery knob; a tuberous root vegetable with brown skin, white flesh and a celery-like flavour.

CHEESE

cheddar the most widely eaten cheese in the world; a semi-hard cow's milk cheese originally made in Cheddar, Dorset. We used a low-fat variety with a fat content of not more than 7g per 25g.

cream cheese commonly known as Philadelphia; a mild-flavoured fresh cheese made of cow's milk. It is an acid curd cheese that needs a starter culture of bacteria. We used one with 21g fat per 100g.

feta a crumbly goat's or sheep's milk cheese with a sharp salty taste.

goat's made from goat's milk, has a strong, earthy taste; available in both soft and firm textures, sometimes rolled in ash or herbs.

mozzarella this soft, spun-curd cheese originated in southern Italy where it is traditionally made from water buffalo milk. Cow's milk versions of this product, commonly known as pizza cheese, are available. We used one with 17.5g fat per 100g.

ricotta a low-fat, fresh unripened cheese with 3g fat per 100g.

CHERVIL also known as cicily; mildly fennel-flavoured herb with curly dark-green leaves.

CHICKPEAS also called garbanzos, hummus or channa; an irregularly round, sandy-coloured legume used extensively in Mediterranean and Latin cooking.

CHILLI Use rubber gloves when seeding and chopping fresh chillies as they can burn your skin. Removing seeds and membranes lessens the heat level.

flakes crushed dried chillies.

green generally unripened thai chillies, but different varieties that are ripe when green may be used, such as habanero, poblano or serrano chillies.thai, red small, medium hot, and bright red in colour.

CHINESE BROCCOLI also known as gai larn; used more for its stems than coarse leaves.

CHINESE CABBAGE also known as peking cabbage, wong bok or petsai. Elongated in shape with pale green, crinkly leaves. Can be shredded or chopped and eaten raw or braised, steamed or stir-fried.

CHOY SUM also known as flowering pak choy or flowering white cabbage.

CIABATTA in Italian, the word means slipper, which is the traditional shape of this crisp-crusted white bread.

CIDER a beverage made by pressing the juice from apples. Alcoholic content ranges widely.

CINNAMON STICK the dried inner bark of the shoots of the cinnamon tree.

COCOA POWDER also known as cocoa; dried, unsweetened, roasted and ground cocoa beans.

COCONUT

cream is obtained commercially from the first pressing of the coconut flesh alone, without the addition of water.

shredded thin strips of dried coconut.

COOKING-OIL SPRAY we used a cholesterol-free cooking spray made from rapeseed oil.

CORIANDER also known as cilantro or chinese parsley; bright-green leafed herb with a pungent flavour. Often stirred into or sprinkled over a dish just before serving for maximum impact. Both the stems and roots are also used in Thai cooking; wash well before chopping.

CORNFLOUR also known as cornstarch; used as a thickening agent in all types of cooking.

CORNICHON French for gherkin, a tiny variety of cucumber. Pickled, they are a traditional accompaniment to pâté.

CORNMEAL ground dried corn (maize); available in different textures.

COURGETTE also called zucchini. A member of the squash family, having edible flowers.

COUSCOUS a fine, grain-like cereal product, made from semolina. Originally from North Africa.

CUMIN also known as zeera, available in seed or ground form.

CURLY ENDIVE also known as frisee, a curly-leafed green vegetable, mainly used in salads.

CURRANTS dried, tiny, almost black raisins so-named after a grape variety that originated in Corinth, Greece.

CURRY PASTE

tikka masala literally meaning blended spices; a masala can be whole spices, a paste or a powder, and can include herbs as well as spices and other seasonings. Traditional dishes are usually based on and named after particular masalas. The word tikka means a bite-sized piece of meat, poultry or fish, or sometimes a cutlet. So, a jar labelled tikka masala usually contains the manufacturer's choice of spices and oils, mixed together to make a paste.

DASHI basic seaweed and fish stock. Made from dried bonito (fish) flakes and kelp (kombu). Instant dashi powder, also known as dashi-no-moto, is a concentrated granulated powder. Available from Asian specialty stores.

ESSENCES also known as extracts; generally the by-product of distillation of plants.

FENNEL also known as finocchio or anise; eaten raw in salads or braised or fried as a vegetable accompaniment. Also the name given to dried seeds having a licorice flavour.

FLOUR

buckwheat although not a true cereal, flour is made from buckwheat seeds. Available from health food stores.

plain an all-purpose flour, made from wheat.

self-raising plain flour sifted with baking powder (1 cup flour to 2 teaspoons baking powder).

FOCACCIA a flat Italian-style bread.

GAI LARN also known as gai lum, kanah, or chinese kale; appreciated more for its stems than its coarse leaves. Serve steamed and stir-fried, in soups and noodle dishes. Available from Asian food stores and many greengrocers.

GELATINE we used powdered gelatine; also available in sheet form known as leaf gelatine.

GINGER

fresh also known as green or root ginger. Can be kept, peeled, covered with dry sherry, in a jar and refrigerated, or frozen in an airtight container.

ground also known as powdered ginger; cannot be substituted for fresh ginger.

pickled available, packaged, from Asian food stores; pickled paper-thin shavings of ginger preserved in a mixture of vinegar, sugar and natural colouring.

GOLDEN SYRUP by-product of refined sugarcane; pure maple syrup or honey can be substituted.

GREEN SPLIT PEAS also known as field peas; green or yellow pulse grown especially for drying, split in half along a centre seam.

HAM we used light ham with a fat content of 2.3g per 100g, about half that of regular ham.

HARISSA sauce or paste made from dried red chillies, garlic, oil and sometimes caraway seeds.

HERBS when specified, we used dried (not ground) herbs in the proportion of 1:4 for fresh herbs (1 teaspoon dried herbs equals 4 teaspoons chopped fresh herbs).

HORSERADISH CREAM a paste made of grated horseradish, oil, mustard seeds and sugar.

HUMMUS a Middle Eastern dip or salad made from chickpeas, garlic, lemon juice and tahini (sesame seed paste).

JUICE, FRESH we made our own fresh juice in every recipe.

KAFFIR LIME LEAVES look like two glossy dark green leaves joined end to end, forming a rounded hourglass shape. Sold fresh, dried or frozen; the dried leaves are less potent so double the number called for in a recipe if you substitute them for fresh leaves. A strip of fresh lime peel may be substituted for each kaffir lime leaf.

KECAP MANIS Indonesian sweet, thick soy sauce which has sugar and spices added.

KIRSCH cherry-flavoured liqueur. kiwi fruit also known as chinese gooseberry.

LAVASH flat, unleavened bread, originally from the Mediterranean.

LEMONGRASS a tall, clumping, lemon-smelling and tasting, sharp-edged grass; the white lower part of each stem is finely chopped and used in Asian cooking or for tea.

LENTILS (red, brown, yellow) dried pulses often identified by and named after their colour.french green originally from France, these are a small, dark-green, fast-cooking lentils with a delicate flavour.

LIGHT SOURED CREAM we used a low-fat sour cream having a fat content of 18.5g per 100g.

LINGUINE long, narrow pasta often thought of as a flat spaghetti.

LOW-FAT CREAM we used cream having a fat content of 18%.

LOW-FAT DAIRY-FREE SPREAD we used a spread with a fat content of 2.4g per 5g of spread (47g of fat per 100g of spread).

LOW-FAT MAYONNAISE we used cholesterol-free mayonnaise having less than 3g fat per 100g.

LOW-FAT WHIPPING CREAM we used cream with a fat content of 18%.

LOW-FAT YOGURT we used yogurt having a fat content of less than 0.2%.

LYCHEES delicious fruit with a light texture and flavour; peel away rough skin, remove seed and use. Also available in cans.

MANDARIN also known as tangerine; a small, loose-skinned citrus fruit. Segments in a light syrup are available canned.

MANGETOUT ('eat all'), also called snow peas. Mangetout tendrils, the growing shoots of the plant, are sold by greengrocers.

MANGO tropical fruit with skin colour ranging from green through yellow to deep red. Its fragrant deep yellow flesh surrounds a large flat seed. Mango cheeks in a light syrup are available canned.

MAPLE SYRUP distilled sap of the maple tree. Maple-favoured syrup is made from cane sugar and artificial maple flavouring and is not a substitute for the real thing.

MIRIN a champagne-coloured Japanese cooking wine made expressly for cooking and should not be confused with sake.

MIXED SPICE a blend of ground spices usually consisting of cinnamon, allspice and nutmeg.

MUSHROOMS

button small, cultivated white mushrooms having a delicate, subtle flavour.

chestnut light to dark brown mushrooms with full-bodied flavour. Button or cup mushrooms can be substituted for chestnut mushrooms.

flat large, flat mushrooms with a rich earthy flavour; sometimes misnamed field mushrooms, which are wild mushrooms.

oyster also known as abalone; a grey-white mushroom shaped like a fan. Smooth, with a subtle, oyster-like flavour.

portobello large, dark brown mushrooms possessing a robust, full-bodied flavour, they are ideal for filling or barbecuing.

shiitake when fresh are also known as chinese black, forest or golden oak mushrooms; they have an earthy taste. When dried, are known as donko or dried chinese mushrooms; rehydrate before use.

MUSTARD, AMERICAN a sweet yellow mixture containing mustard seeds, sugar, salt, spices and garlic.

NASHI PEAR also called japanese or asian pear; a member of the pear family, but similar in appearance to an apple.

NOODLES

fresh rice thick, wide, almost white in colour; made from rice and vegetable oil. Must be covered with boiling water to remove starch and excess oil before using in soups and stir-fries.

hokkien also known as stir-fry noodles; fresh wheat noodles resembling thick, yellow-brown spaghetti and needing no pre-cooking before use.

rice stick a dried noodle, available flat and wide or very thin; made from rice flour and water.

rice vermicelli also known as rice-flour noodles and rice-stick noodles; made from ground rice. Sold dried, these noodles are best either deep-fried, or soaked then stir-fried or used in soups.

soba thin spaghetti-like pale brown noodle from Japan made from varying amounts of buckwheat and wheat flour. Used in soups and stir-fries.

NORI a type of dried seaweed often used in Japanese cooking. Sold in thin sheets.

NUTMEG available whole or in ground form.

OIL

grapeseed made from grape seeds. Available from most supermarkets.

groundnut pressed from ground peanuts; has high smoke point (capacity to handle high heat without burning).

olive made from ripened olives. Extra virgin and virgin are the first and second press, respectively, of the olives, while extra light or light refers to taste, not fat levels.

sesame made from roasted, crushed white sesame seeds.

walnut made from walnuts.

ONION

brown and white are interchangeable. Their pungent flesh adds flavour to a vast range of dishes.

red also known as spanish, red spanish or bermuda onion; a sweet, large, purple-red onion that is particularly good eaten raw in salads.

shallots also called french shallots, golden shallots or eschalots; small, elongated, brown-skinned members of the onion family. Grows in tight clusters similar to garlic.

spring also known as scallion; onions with small white bulbs, long green leaves and narrow green-leafed tops.

PAK CHOY also known as bok choy, pak choi, chinese white cabbage or chinese chard; has a fresh, mild mustard taste. Use both stems and leaves.

baby pak choy also known as pak kat farang or shanghai pak choy; is small and more tender than pak choy.

PAPAYA also known as pawpaw; a large, pear-shaped red-orange tropical fruit. Sometimes used unripened (green) in cooking.

PAPRIKA ground, dried, red pepper, available sweet or hot.

PARSLEY, FLAT-LEAF also known as continental parsley or italian parsley.

PASSIONFRUIT also known as granadilla; a small tropical fruit, native to Brazil, comprised of a tough dark-purple skin surrounding edible black sweet-sour seeds.

PATTY-PAN SQUASH also known as crookneck or custard marrow pumpkins; a round, slightly flat summer squash being yellow to pale-green in colour and having a scalloped edge. Harvested young, it has firm white flesh and distinct flavour.

PECANS native to the United States; buttery, golden-brown and rich. Good in savoury as well as sweet dishes; especially good in salads.

PEPITAS dried pumpkin seeds.

PEPPER also known as bell pepper or capsicum. Native to Central and South America. Discard seeds and membranes before use.

PEPPERCORNS, BLACK the strongest flavoured of all the pepper-corn varieties. They are picked when the berries are not quite ripe, then dried until they shrivel and the skin turns dark brown or black.

PIDE also known as turkish bread, comes in long (about 45cm) flat loaves as well as individual rounds. This bread is made from wheat flour and sprinkled with sesame or black onion seeds.

PINE NUTS a small, cream-coloured kernel from pine cones; known as pignoli.

PISTACHIOS pale green, delicately flavoured nut inside hard, off-white shell. To peel, soak shelled nuts in boiling water for about 5 minutes; drain, pat dry with absorbent paper, then rub skins with cloth to peel.

PITTA also spelled pita and known as lebanese bread, this unleavened wheat-flour pocket bread is sold in large, flat pieces that separate easily into two thin rounds. Also available in a small thick variety known as pocket pitta.

POLENTA also known as cornmeal; a flour-like cereal made of dried corn (maize) sold ground in several different textures; also the name of the dish made from it.

PRESERVED LEMON whole or quartered salted lemons preserved in a mixture of olive oil and lemon juice; imparts a rich, salty-sour acidic flavour. Available from good food shops and delicatessens. Rinse well under cold water before using.

PROSCIUTTO cured, air-dried (unsmoked), pressed ham.

PRUNES commercially or sun-dried plums.

RADICCHIO a member of the chicory family. Has dark burgundy leaves and a strong bitter flavour.

RAISINS large, dark-brown, dried, sweet grapes.

RHUBARB a vegetable related to sorrel; only the firm, reddish stems are eaten. It's normally sweetened and eaten as a dessert.

RICE

arborio small, round-grain rice well-suited to absorb a large amount of liquid; especially suitable for making risottos.

basmati a white fragrant long-grain rice. It should be washed several times before cooking.

brown long-grain entire grain with only the inedible outer husk removed; nutritious and high in fibre. Has a nutlike flavour and chewy texture. The elongated grains remain separate when cooked.

jasmine a fragrant long-grain rice; white rice can be substituted but will not taste the same.

koshihikari small, round-grain white rice. May be substituted with short-grain white rice.

RICE PAPER SHEETS mostly from Vietnam (banh trang). Made from rice paste and stamped into rounds, with a woven pattern. Stores well at room temperature, although are quite brittle and break easily. Dipped momentarily in water, they become pliable wrappers for fried food and for wrapping around fresh (uncooked) vegetables.

RISONI also known as risi; small rice-shaped pasta very similar to another small pasta, orzo. Any small soup pasta can be substituted for risoni.

ROCKET also known as arugula, rugula or rucola; a peppery-tasting green leaf which can be used in a similar way to baby spinach leaves. Can be used raw in salads or used in cooking. Baby rocket leaves are both smaller and less peppery in taste.

ROLLED GRAINS includes rice, barley, oats, rye and triticale; the whole grain has been steamed and flattened – not the quick-cook variety. Available from health food stores and supermarkets.

ROSEWATER extract made from crushed rose petals; used for its aromatic quality in many desserts and sweets.

SAKE Japanese rice wine. If unavailable, dry sherry, vermouth or brandy may be substituted.

SALTED BLACK BEANS also known as Chinese black beans, these are fermented and salted soy beans available in cans and jars.

Used most often in Asian cooking; chop before, or mash during, cooking to release flavour.

SAMBAL OELEK also spelled ulek or olek; a salty paste made from ground chillies and vinegar.

SAUCES

barbecue a spicy tomato-based sweet sauce used to marinate or baste, or as an accompaniment.

cranberry made of cranberries cooked in sugar syrup; has an astringent flavour.

fish also called nam pla or nuoc nam; made from pulverised salted fermented fish, most often anchovies. Has a pungent smell and strong taste; use sparingly.

kecap manis a dark, thick, sweet soy sauce used in most South-East Asian cuisines.

oyster Asian in origin, this rich, brown sauce is made from oysters and their brine, cooked with salt and soy sauce, and thickened with starches.

soy made from fermented soy beans. Many variations are available in most supermarkets; we used a mild Japanese variety.

sweet chilli a relatively mild, Thai-type sauce made from red chillies, sugar, garlic and vinegar.

tomato pasta sauce, bottled prepared sauce available from supermarkets; sometimes labelled sugo.

SEED TAPIOCA sometimes called sago because it comes from the sago palm pearl; tapioca is from the root of the cassava plant. Used in soups, desserts and often as a thickening agent; available from some supermarkets and most health-food stores.

SEMOLINA made from durum wheat; milled various-textured granules, all of these finer than flour. The main ingredient in good pastas, in some kinds of gnocchi and in many Middle-Eastern and Indian sweets.

SESAME SEEDS black and white are the most common, however there are red and brown varieties

also. To toast: spread seeds evenly on oven tray, toast in moderate oven briefly.

SICHUAN PEPPERCORNS also known as szechuan or chinese pepper. Small, red-brown aromatic seeds with a distinctive mild peppery-lemon flavour.

SKEWERS bamboo or metal skewers can be used. Rub oil onto metal skewers to stop meat sticking. Soak bamboo skewers in water for at least 1 hour before use to prevent splintering and scorching.

SKIMMED MILK we used milk with a fat content of 0.15% or lower.

SOURED CREAM, LIGHT we used a low-fat sour cream having a fat content of 18.5g per 100g.

SPECIAL K low-fat breakfast cereal based on rice and wheat; good source of calcium and iron.

SPINACH also known as English spinach and, incorrectly, silverbeet. The tender green leaves are good raw in salads or added to soups and stir-fries just before serving.

SPLIT PEAS also known as field peas. A green or yellow pulse used in soups and stews

SPONGE FINGER BISCUITS also known as savoy biscuits, lady's fingers or sponge fingers; Italian-style crisp fingers made from sponge cake mixture.

STAR ANISE a star-shaped pod whose seeds have an astringent aniseed flavour; used to flavour stocks.

STOCK 1 cup (250ml) stock is equivalent to 1 cup (250ml) water plus 1 crumbled stock cube. It may be more convenient to use stock in cartons.

SUGAR we used coarse granulated table sugar, also known as crystal sugar, unless stated otherwise.

brown a soft, fine granulated sugar retaining molasses for its characteristic colour and flavour.

caster also known as superfine or finely granulated table sugar.

icing sugar also known as confectioners' sugar or powdered sugar.

palm also known as nam tan pip, jaggery or gula melaka. Sold in rock-hard cakes; can be substituted with brown sugar.

raw natural brown granulated sugar.

SUGAR SNAP PEAS also known as honey snap peas; fresh small pea that can be eaten whole.

SULTANAS small dried grapes, also known as golden raisins.

SUMAC a purple-red, astringent spice ground from berries growing on Mediterranean shrubs; adds a tart flavour to dips and dressings. Available from Middle-Eastern food stores.

SUNFLOWER SEED KERNELS kernels from dried, husked sunflower seeds.

SWEDES also known as rutabaga, swedes have a yellow skin and look similar to turnips.

SWISS CHARD also known as seakale or silverbeet. A green-leafed vegetable with sturdy celery-like white stems. Can be used similarly to spinach.

TACO SHELLS commercially prepared deep-fried corn tortillas folded over to create a container for various fillings.

TAHINI sesame seed paste available from Middle-Eastern food stores; most often used in hummus, baba ghanoush and other Lebanese recipes.

TAMARI a thick, dark sauce made mainly from soy beans. Has a distinctive mellow flavour. Is used mainly used as a dipping sauce or for basting. Available from most supermarkets and Asian food stores.

TAMARIND PASTE made from the pods of a tree native to India that contain a sour-sweet pulp that is dried then reconstituted to make the dark, thick paste that adds a tangy astringent taste to curries. It can also be used in marinades and bastes for meats.

TANGELO a cross between a grapefruit and tangerine; a loose-skinned, juicy, sweetly-tart citrus fruit with few seeds. Is eaten like an orange.

TENDERSTEM BROCCOLI a cross between broccoli and Chinese kale, is milder and sweeter than broccoli. Each long stem is topped by a loose floret that closely resembles broccoli. Tenderstem broccoli is completely edible, from floret to stem. Substitute broccoli if you are unable to find it.

THAI BASIL has smaller leaves and purplish stems. It has a slight licorice or aniseed taste, and is often used in Thai cuisine.

TOFU also known as bean curd, an off-white, custard-like product made from the milk of crushed soy beans; comes fresh (as soft or firm), and processed) as fried or pressed dried sheets). Silken tofu refers to the method by which it is made, where it is strained through silk.

TOMATO

cherry also known as Tiny Tim or Tom Thumb tomatoes; small and round.

plum also called egg or Roma; these are smallish oval-shaped tomatoes much used in Italian cooking or salads.

TORTILLA unleavened bread originating in Mexico; made from either wheat or corn.

TRITICALE a nutritious hybrid of wheat (triticum) and rye (secale) which contains more protein and less gluten than wheat and has a nutty, sweet flavour. Available in whole grain, flour and flakes.

TURMERIC also known as kamin; related to galangal and ginger. Must be grated or pounded to release its somewhat acrid aroma and pungent flavour. Fresh turmeric may be substituted with dried turmeric powder (2 teaspoons of ground turmeric plus a teaspoon of sugar for every 20g of fresh turmeric called for in a recipe).

TZATZIKI Greek yogurt and cucumber dish sometimes containing mint and/or garlic.

UNPROCESSED BRAN made from the outer layer of a cereal – most often the husks of wheat, rice or oats.

VANILLA POD dried, long, thin pod from a tropical orchid grown in Central and South America and Tahiti; the tiny black seeds inside the bean are used to impart a vanilla flavour in baking and desserts. Place whole bean in a container of sugar to make the vanilla sugar called for in recipes.

VANILLA EXTRACT vanilla beans infused in alcohol and water.

VIETNAMESE MINT not actually a mint at all, this narrow-leafed, pungent herb, also known as Cambodian mint and laksa leaf (daun laksa), is widely used in many Asian soups and salads.

VINE LEAVES available fresh or vacuum-packed in brine. Available from Middle-Eastern food stores.

VINEGAR

balsamic authentic only from the province of Modena, Italy; made from a regional wine of white Trebbiano grapes specially processed then aged in antique wooden casks to give the exquisite pungent flavour.

cider made from fermented apples.

red wine based on fermented red wine.

white wine made from fermented white wine.

WAKAME a bright-green seaweed, is usually sold in dry form and used in soups, salads and seasonings. Dried wakame must be softened by soaking for about 10 minutes then discarding any hard stems. Wakame can be found in most asian food stores.

WALNUTS a rich, flavourful nut. Store in the refrigerator because of its high oil content.

WATERCRESS one of the cress family, a large group of peppery greens used raw in salads, dips and sandwiches, or cooked in soups. Highly perishable, so must be used as soon as possible after purchase.

WHEAT GERM small creamy flakes milled from the embryo of the berry.

YOGURT we used either sheep's or goat's milk yogurt in this book.

index

conversion charts

MEASURING EQUIPMENT

The cup and spoon measurements used in this book are metric: one measuring cup holds approximately 250ml; one metric tablespoon holds 20ml; one metric teaspoon holds 5ml.

HOW TO MEASURE

The most accurate way of measuring dry ingredients is to weigh them. When using graduated metric measuring cups, shake dry ingredients loosely into the appropriate cup. Do not tap the cup on a bench or tightly pack the ingredients unless directed to do so. Level top of measuring cups and spoons with a knife. When measuring liquids, place a clear glass or plastic jug with metric markings on a flat surface to check accuracy at eye level. We use large eggs having an average weight of 60g.

WARNING This book may contain recipes for dishes made with raw or lightly cooked eggs. These should be avoided by vulnerable people such as pregnant and nursing mothers, invalids, the elderly, babies and young children.

DRY MEASURES

METRIC	IMPERIAL
15g	½oz
30g	1oz
60g	2oz
90g	3oz
125g	4oz (¼lb)
155g	5oz
185g	6oz
220g	7oz
250g	8oz (½lb)
280g	9oz
315g	10oz
345g	11oz
375g	12oz (¾lb)
410g	13oz
440g	14oz
470g	15oz
500g	16oz (1lb)
750g	24oz (1½lb)
1kg	32oz (2lb)

LIQUID MEASURES

METRIC	IMPERIAL
30ml	1 fluid oz
60ml	2 fluid oz
100ml	3 fluid oz
125ml	4 fluid oz
150ml	5 fluid oz (¼ pint/1 gill)
190ml	6 fluid oz
250ml	8 fluid oz
300ml	10 fluid oz (½ pint)
500ml	16 fluid oz
600ml	20 fluid oz (1 pint)
1000ml (1 litre)	1¾ pints

LENGTH MEASURES

METRIC	IMPERIAL
3mm	⅛in
6mm	¼in
1cm	½in
2cm	¾in
2.5cm	1in
5cm	2in
6cm	2½in
8cm	3in
10cm	4in
13cm	5in
15cm	6in
18cm	7in
20cm	8in
23cm	9in
25cm	10in
28cm	11in
30cm	12in (1ft)

OVEN TEMPERATURES

These oven temperatures are only a guide for conventional ovens.
For fan-forced ovens, check the manufacturer's manual.

	°C (CELSIUS)	°F (FAHRENHEIT)	GAS MARK
Very low	120	250	½
Low	150	275-300	1-2
Moderately low	170	325	3
Moderate	180	350-375	4-5
Moderately hot	200	400	6
Hot	220	425-450	7-8
Very hot	240	475	9

ACP Books
General manager Christine Whiston
Test kitchen food director Pamela Clark
Editorial director Susan Tomnay
Creative director Hieu Chi Nguyen
Director of sales Brian Cearnes
Marketing manager Bridget Cody
Business analyst Rebecca Varela
Operations manager David Scotto
International rights enquiries Laura Bamford
lbamford@acpuk.com

ACP Books are published by ACP Magazines a division of PBL Media Pty Limited

Group publisher, Women's lifestyle Pat Ingram
Director of sales, Women's lifestyle Lynette Phillips
Commercial manager, Women's lifestyle
Seymour Cohen
Marketing director, Women's lifestyle Matthew Dominello
Public relations manager, Women's lifestyle
Hannah Deveraux
Creative director, Events, Women's lifestyle
Luke Bonnano
Research Director, Women's lifestyle Justin Stone
ACP Magazines, Chief Executive officer Scott Lorson
PBL Media, Chief Executive officer Ian Law

Produced by ACP Books, Sydney.
Published by ACP Books, a division of
ACP Magazines Ltd, 54 Park St, Sydney;
GPO Box 4088, Sydney, NSW 2001.
phone (02) 9282 8618 fax (02) 9267 9438.
acpbooks@acpmagazines.com.au
www.acpbooks.com.au
Printed and bound in China.

Australia Distributed by Network Services,
phone +61 2 9282 8777 fax +61 2 9264 3278
networkweb@networkservicescompany.com.au
United Kingdom Distributed by Australian Consolidated
Press (UK),
phone (01604) 642 200 fax (01604) 642 300
books@acpuk.com
New Zealand Distributed by Netlink Distribution Company,
phone (9) 366 9966 ask@ndc.co.nz
South Africa Distributed by PSD Promotions,
phone (27 11) 392 6065/6/7 fax (27 11) 392 6079/80
orders@psdprom.co.za
Canada Distributed by Publishers Group Canada
phone (800) 663 5714 fax (800) 565 3770
service@raincoast.com

A catalogue record for this book is available from the British Library.
ISBN 978-1-903777-45-9
© ACP Magazines Ltd 2008
ABN 18 053 273 546
This publication is copyright. No part of it may be reproduced or
transmitted in any form without the written permission of the publishers.